mily Christm

Your grandmother spends half an hour closely examining the array of drinks on offer before asking for the only one you haven't got. *Miss a turn* whilst you roam the street canvassing the neighbours for a bottle of Wincarnis Egg Nog.

Your brother-in-law turns up with two cans of McEwans Lager, puts them on the kitchen table, then helps himself to repeated large glasses of your 10 year-old Glenfiddich. *Miss a turn* whilst you fume.

8

You return from the toilet to find your brother-in-law sitting in your chair, holding the TV remote control. *Miss a turn* whilst you fume at him in his fucking grey slip-on shoes.

Your auntie gives you a pair of grey nylon socks as a gift. You successfully feign an expression of pleasure and gratitude which doesn't look sarcastic. *Move forward one space.*

You are eating some chocolate raisins when your sister starts changing her baby's shitty nappy right under your nose on the coffee table. *Go back two squares.*

12

You notice that your brother-in-law 's fucking grey slip-on shoes have got them little fucking gold chains across the top. *Miss a turn* whilst you fantasise about smashing his head repeatedly against the wall.

14

Have a nut.

You pretend to go out to buy a paper and spend a lovely 30 minutes round the corner sitting in the car having a fag. *Move forward two spaces.*

You've bought your mother-in-law a string of freshwater pearls costing the best part of £80, and she's bought you a soap-on-a-rope. She feels awful. *Move forward two spaces.*

Your brother-in-law starts talking about the satellite navigation system in his new Rover 75. *Miss a turn* whilst you sit and stare at his fucking cravat.

You are shaken from a doze to play Monopoly with three over-excited 5-year-olds. Despite your best efforts to lose quickly, you are embroiled in a four-hour marathon complete with random rule changes and tantrums. *Miss a turn.*

You have to go into the shed for a fag because your elderly mum thinks you gave up smoking 12 years ago. *Miss a turn.*

Your mum turns the film off to watch the Queen's speech. After 5 minutes of fuming, you turn to notice that she is fast asleep. Put the film back on in time for the closing credits and *miss a turn.*

21

Have another nut.

Your uncle is a Christian, and the fear that he's going to say grace is spoiling your anticipation of Christmas dinner. *Move back one space.*

At dinner, there aren't enough chairs. *Miss a turn* whilst you sit on a deckchair with four cushions, and your chin just reaching the edge of the table. And your brother-in-law's got the carver, so *miss another turn.*

Your mother arrives and starts singing your brother-in-law's praises. *Miss a turn.*

25

Have a Quality Street.

You sit clenching a can of warm McEwans lager and watch your brother-in-law cheerfully opening the bottle of Jack Daniels that you had hidden under the stairs. *Miss two turns.*

23

Have a matchmaker.

Every day I wander down our garden to write in an upmarket shed overlooking a ravishing Cotswold valley. Whenever I'm sad, weary or de... ...e however, it is not the stunning views out of all four window... ...ee pages from Viz which my son Felix had framed f... ...hang or... ...gh over the years I have memorised e... ...fail to make me laugh.

...ning private let-

...od, arriving in ...on a spiffing ...s the envy of ...on the covet- ...and Jesus to

...r the same ...a bishop,

...d, Timmy ...her house ...never far away

Wher... ...ication. During... ...nd the row was...

Viz work... ...ge of witty text...

The editor... Thus my dis... discover a... Gloucestershi...

Having just be... by so many teac... dreadful friends.

No magazine d... of political correc... lesbian, paedophi...

The joy of Viz is... gasps turn into sc... Mum's browning fa... Prince Edward to i...

I am therefore thrille... ...g as the bear comes to no harm). This new annua... ...hat has delighted us in past issues - and may Viz lighten ou... ...come.

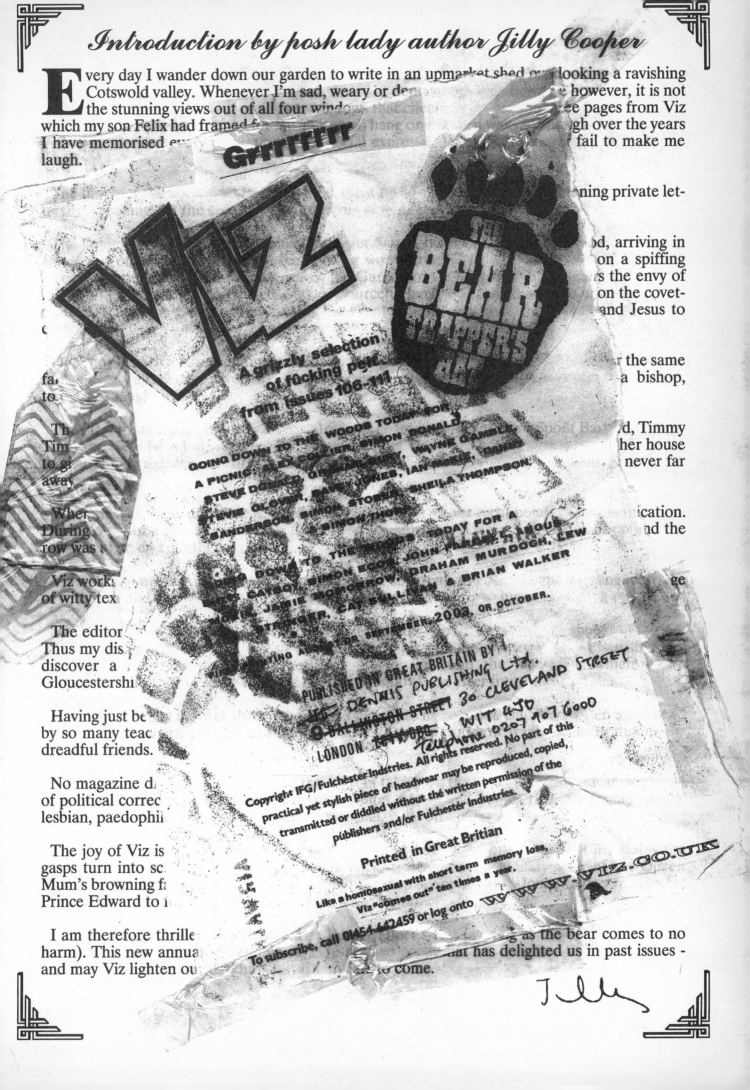

Grrrrrrrr

Viz

A grizzly selection of fucking pe... from issues 106-111

GOING DOWN TO THE WOODS TODAY FOR... ...SIMON DONALD, A PICNIC: ALEX COLLIER, ...WAYNE GAMBLE, DAN... STEVE DONALD, GR... ...IAN McKIE, SANDERSON, SIMON STOR... SHEILA THOMPSON, & SIMON THOR...

...S TODAY FOR A ...OG DOWARD, ...JOHN FARD... ...CAT... SIMON ECOT... GRAHAM MURDOCH, LEW ...R JAMIE MORROR... ...AM & BRIAN WALKER ...ER, CAT SULLIV... ...SEPTEMBER 2003, OR OCTOBER.

Letterbocks

Star Letter

- Given the current strains on the penal system, surely lighter, more jokey type sentences could be introduced for 'lovable rogue' type criminals.

**Big Nige
Wakefield**

- I am a teacher, and last week I confiscated a Jazz Mag from one of my pupils. Imagine my disappointment when I took it in the stockroom for a crafty shuffle.

Have you ever tried unloading your pods over a picture of Louis Armstrong and an article about clarinet reeds?

**Gary
Jesmond**

- Two years ago, I invested in a 'limited edition' Orange Kit-Kat. Could any of your readers advise me on the profit of this speculation?

**Adrian Newth
e-mail**

Towed rage

- I was driving home from holiday last summer when I realised I was being 'tailgated' by a white van. He ignored all my signals for him to pass, and for an hour we tried to lose the maniac. Eventually I pulled over to have words. How foolish I felt when I realised it was the caravan we were towing. Do I win £5, or is it one of those mugs?

**Steve Cade
Manchester**

A brief waste of time

- I tell you what, that Jamie Oliver, he's a cunt, isn't he. Getting off with his grandma and all that. Cooking is for pansies, mate. Go and get yourself a proper job.

**L. Beyan
Stoke on Trent**

Play it again

- On November 26th last year, I was playing cricket with friends on my back lawn when I took a stunning catch. Starting from my position of wicket keeper, I dived full stretch to catch the ball one handed, millimetres from the ground at around short extra cover. The feat was all the more remarkable as I had consumed 7 pints of lager in the previous hour. I was wondering if any countries had military or spy satellites orbiting the south of New Zealand at the time which may have captured footage of my logic-defying catch. If so, could I please have a copy?

**Antony Peterson
Invercargill, NZ**

- Every time I check my answer machine messages, there's always one from Professor Steven Hawking, informing me of the time and day that he called. No offence to Mr Hawking, but I feel his messages are a waste of tape space. He should get back to solving the mysteries of the universe and leave me alone.

**Ben Cormack
Castle Douglas**

- I shagged that Lindsey Dawn McKenzie on stage at a Sunday Sport Roadshow a few years ago, and she was rubbish.

**Tom
Newcastle**

- I was clearing out my shed last week when I found The Lord Jesus Christ, son of God stuck in a corner behind the lawnmower.

**S. Paine
e-mail**

* *Have you found anyone unusual in your garden shed? Perhaps you spotted Adolf Hitler behind some plant pots, or maybe you came across Rasputin all tangled up in your hosepipe. Send your pictures to the usual address, and we'll give a Viz disposable cameras to the best ones we receive.*

- 'Mr. Muscle loves the jobs you hate', the advert says. Oh yes? Well I haven't noticed it volunteer to suck my husband's sweaty cock every Friday night when he comes up to bed after watching Eurotrash.

**Mrs. E. Gaines
London**

Say 'Processed Cheese'

I'm only insincere for the beer

of *Who Wants To Be A Millionaire?*

**Andrew Denny
Narrowboat Granny**

- Here's the Prime minister making his second appearance in Insincere Smile Corner. Watch as this grin turns into a grimace of fear.

**K.D. Stewart
Edinburgh**

- Here's a pic showing Chris Tarrant 'happily' giving away about half of what he probably earns for every episode

- Look at this one. He looks like he's half way through the metamorphosis in *An American Werewolf in London*.

**Jarv
Mansfield**

Fat tants

● I've discovered this picture of a real life Millie Tant (right), and her equally lardy mate. Do I win a prize ?

Mark Prince
e-mail

● I was amazed to see the incredible prices of personalised car registration plates in an advert recently. However, Halfords kindly did me a set of "AN 1" for £15, saving me about £20,000.

Adrian Newth
Worcester

Box clever

● Now that such a large percentage of the population own their own mobile phones, surely it is time British Telecom erected mobile phone boxes to allow the general public reliable access to this popular modern communication system.

Tom Rice
Manchester

Ham & eggo

● Can any of your clever dick readers explain to me why the 'protective atmosphere' sliced ham is packed in smells like somebody has just farted in the packet. Or do you not give a shit about what goes on in sliced ham packing factories?

M. Hunt
e-mail

* Do *you* care what goes on in sliced ham packing factories? Call 0207 565 3271 and listen to the taped message. To register your vote say 'YES' if you do care what goes on in sliced ham packing factories, or 'NO' if you don't give a toss. If an Irishman answers the phone, simply replace the handset and try again later. Calls are charged at the national rate.

● I am sick and tired of hearing wannabe TV and radio stars moaning on about how difficult it is to break into the world of showbiz. You never hear proper stars like Lisa Tarbuck and Zoe Ball complaining, do you? By the way, who is Gail Porter's dad?

Jim
London

● It was lucky for me the other day when a black cat crossed my path. Though not so lucky for him, as I was driving a stolen steamroller with no brakes whilst four times over the limit.

C. de Gaulle
Cheltenham

WIG WATCH

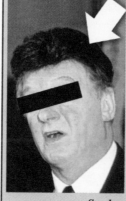

Sender:
M. France, e-mail

Headline News

● With reference to sub-editors slipping rude headlines into their articles, I think the cheeky staff at OK Magazine have done well here. Either that, or they have some real inside information.

R. Donnett, Wimbledon

BARBRA STREISAND
HAS THE PAINTERS IN

Wendall Wall, the man Barbra Streisa accused of stalking her, is suing the di Last January …ll was st….ed by

ings, they've gone for the front page splash.

Max, Beaumaris

● I spotted the above clipping too, only my letter arrived two days after R. Donnett's. Bugger.

Daniel Fox
Cardiff

● What about this one (see right) from the Holyhead and Anglesey Mail. Sod the sub-head-

School site: Parents opposed
MOBILE MAST DEBATE

TOP TIPS

WANT to feel famous? Simply pop down to your local bistro and sit underneath the specials board. People will be continually looking in your direction and making comments.

R. Harron
Brixton

JOURNALISTS for local TV stations. Fool viewers into thinking you have been sent abroad by waiting a few seconds before answering questions the presenter asks you.

Douglas Castle
Beecormack

SUPERMARKETS. Sell your undersized vegetables for twice the price by not cleaning the shit off them and calling them 'organic'.

B. Cormack
Castle Douglas

GARDENERS. Save time cutting your lawn by using a strimmer. Simply pull the cord out to about 20 feet in length, start the strimmer and jump out of the way. Hey presto! a 40 foot diameter lawn cut in seconds. (This works best with circular lawns).

Rob Coxon
Sheffield

POSTMEN. Increase your chances of receiving a Christmas tip from grateful customers by not being such a fucking misery for the other 51 weeks of the year.

Warwick Sloss
Bristol

LORRY drivers. Save pounds by spending less on pornography and axes to kill women with.

Ian Corrigan
e-mail

● I recently spotted this hotel whilst driving through Gateshead and wondered if any Viz readers know of a more inappropriately named establishment.

Geoff Grapes
Macclesfield

* Have you spotted any establishments where the name writes cheques that the premises can't cash. Send your pics to 'Polished Turds', PO Box 1PT, Newcastle upon Tyne NE99 1PT. We'll give a disposable camera for the best we receive.

WELL, HOW WAS SHE? GOOD? BAD..?

MEDIUM

MADAM OLGA CONTACTS THE DEAD

OH, LORDY, IT'S THE FAT SLAGS

THE SUMMER is with us again, and that can mean only *one thing* - Sun, Sea and Sand. So that's three. We know all about the sun and the sea, but what about sand? Children play with it on the beach, balloonists drop it out of bags, and calendar models have it glued to their arse cheeks. It's all around us, on our beaches, in our shoes and on the sides of our matchboxes. But how much do we *really* know about this grittiest of substances? Here are...

20 THINGS YOU NEVER KNEW *about* SAND

SAND

1 If you looked at it under a microscope, you would be amazed to see that sand is made out of countless tiny little irregular shaped rocks, each one no bigger than a grain of sand.

2 Every chef who boils an egg has reason to thank the sand in his egg timer. That's because sand takes exactly three minutes to fall down, exactly the same time as it takes to boil an egg.

3 The egg timer is the earliest clock known to man, but the most modern, the quartz watch, also runs on sand. That's because the quartz which powers it is a type of battery-driven sand which changes the numbers on the front by wobbling exactly sixty times a minute.

4 The smallest ever sandcastle was made by the world's smallest man, Calvin Phillips in 1962. Holidaying in Scarborough, he made the little structure by filling a thimble with sand and patting it down with a mustard spoon. Tragically, later that day Phillips was killed when he was trodden on by a donkey.

5 It's an amazing fact that if you picked up a handful of sand on the beach, you would be holding about a million individual grains. Unless you were Jeremy Beadle, in which case it would be about 300,000.

6 Ironically, even though sand is the opposite of water, it is just as good at putting out flames. In many old fashioned offices you will see red fire buckets containing a flame-retardant mixture of sand, fag-ends and phlegm hanging from the walls.

7 The largest grain of sand ever found turned up on Bondi Beach, Australia in 1956. The whopper, nicknamed Big Bruce, measured over 2 cm across and weighed in at a hefty 38 gms. It is currently on display at the

Museum of Geological Sciences, New South Wales. Scientists have estimated that if every grain of sand on Earth was as large as Big Bruce, the planet would fall out of space under its own weight.

8 If you buy a can of coke in a London Strip Club, the burly barman will probably ask you for a bag of sand. Don't offer him a bag of builders' sand or the bouncer will cut your ears off with a razor and force them down your throat. That's because a bag of sand is cockney rhyming slang for a thousand pounds.

9 Unless you live in York, where a bag of sand is an ineffective means of keeping the River Ouse out your sitting room.

10 During the war, mischievous Japanese guards would often sneak up on their prisoners while they were asleep and bury them up to their necks in sand. Then they would wake them up by playfully kicking their teeth in. Nearly sixty years later, many of the survivors have yet to receive any apology or compensation for car keys lost in the sand.

11 Look out of any window and you won't see any sand, unless you live at the beach or a builders' yard - *only you will!* That's because the window itself is made out of a type of see-

Record-breaking sand Big Bruce
(picture: Australian Sand Monthly)

through sand called glass. So in fact, you see sand *every* time you look out of your window.

12 Unless you've got a broken window.

13 Or a perspex one. Or you've gone blind.

14 Hollywood has always had a love affair with sand. Thousands of films have been made about it, for example The Desert Song and many more.

15 Thousands of Red Indian arrows and millions of Japanese bullets couldn't finish off Hollywood iron man John "Duke Ellington" Wayne (real name Shirley Crabtree). However, in 1979 he was finally killed...by some sand! Filming near atom bomb test sites in Nevada, he ate some sand which eventually gave him fatal cancer.

16 The candy-coloured clown who creeps into children's bedrooms late at night is probably the sandman, an imaginary character who sprinkles magic sand into their eyes, sending them to sleep. Either that or it's a disgraced seventies glam rock star hell bent on diddling your kids.

17 Sand played its part in ending World War 2. On June 6th 1944, the battle to liberate Europe from the nazis began in earnest as over a million allied troops landed on the beach in Normandy. It is estimated that at the height of the invasion, the queue for the ice cream van stretched for over four and a half miles.

18 The Eskimos have over 200 words for snow, but not a single word for sand. That's because sand doesn't grow in the North Pole.

19 Scientists have calculated that if all the World's sand was put in an enormous egg timer, it would take exactly three million billion minutes for it to fall through. That's long enough to boil an egg the size of the Moon to perfection. However, you'd then need a spoon as big as the Eiffel Tower to knock the top off, and toast soldiers the size of the Great Wall of China. And butter the size of the Great Pyramid of Cheops.

20 Despite the name, Sandy Toksvig is not a type of toksvig covered with sand. It is in fact a type of short, neckless lesbian on Call My Bluff.

OH DEAR. WE'VE PRINTED THE WRONG ADDRESS FOR OUR 'REAL ALE PUB OF THE YEAR' IN THE NEW GUIDE.

CAMPAIGN FOR REAL ALE

I HOPE THIS DOESN'T CAUSE ANYONE TO END UP GOING TO THE WRONG PUB.

MEANWHILE

ACCORDING TO THE GUIDE, OUR DESTINATION IS NIGH...

THE MURDERER'S ARMS

NO STUDENTS COPPERS OR QUEERS

OHO! HOSTELRY AHOY!

AH. A TRADITIONAL SPIT 'N' SAWDUST BAR. IT REMINDS ME OF A FIRST-RATE ALEHOUSE IN WINCHESTER CALLED THE CASK AND FUGGLE.

I SAMPLED THE ROCHESTER'S AWLD PARTICULAR THERE IN JUNE OF '83. THE LANDLORD'S NAME WAS REG.

GOOD EVENING. WE WOULD LIKE TO PARTAKE OF A TIPPLE OF YOUR VERY REALEST ALES

DO YOU HAVE A BLACKBOARD LISTING THIS WEEK'S GUEST SELECTION?

WE SELL FOSTERS

FOSTERS? AH, THIS WOULD BE JEREMIAH FOSTER, THE WILTSHIRE MICRO-BREWER

I BELIEVE I SUPPED A PINT OR SO OF HIS BISHOP'S CLOUT AT THE BULL TAVERN IN SALISBURY, IN THE SPRING OF '76

YES, HERE WE ARE – 14th MARCH. "A FULL GOLDEN ALE WITH A LONG HOPPY FINISH. 5.5% ABV." YOU WILL SEE THAT MY NOTES ARE SOMEWHAT LAX TOWARDS THE END.

I THINK THAT COULD HAVE SOMETHING TO DO WITH THE QUANTITIES OF SAID BEVERAGE CONSUMED THAT EVENING.

SNORT!

SNURT!

SNARFLE!

ARFLE!

SNORT!

SNURT!

THREE PRELIMINARY SAMPLES OF MISTER FOSTER'S VERY FINEST IT IS, THEN, IF YOU PLEASE.

WE COME EQUIPPED WITH OUR OWN TASTING GLASSES.

PURCHASES MAY WELL ENSUE IF OUR TASTE BUDS ARE SUITABLY TICKLED

THREE HALVES.

TWO POUND FIFTY-FIVE.

SIP! SIP! SIP!

HM. FULL-FLAVOURED AND HOPPY WITH A LONG MALTY FINISH

JOT JOT

JOT JOT

WELL-BALANCED AND SMOOTH, A ROUNDED EASY-QUAFFER. 3.8% ABV

IT IS REDOLENT OF THE BRAKSPEAR'S FULL NOG I IMBIBED AT THE SPILLER'S ARMS IN HOLME LACEY, IN SEPTEMBER '88

THE LANDLORD, A SPLENDID FELLOW NAMED COLIN, WAS GOOD ENOUGH TO SHOW ME AROUND HIS CELLAR

PINT OF LAGER

LAGER! (TITTER)

SNNF!

SNORT! ARF! DEAR ME!

I SEE WE HAVE AN UNBELIEVER IN OUR MIDST. BUT FEAR NOT, MY YOUNG FRIEND, YOU MAY YET BE SAVED

COME QUAFF AWHILE WITH OUR MERRY BAND OF REPROBATES, AND YOU WILL SOON BE INITIATED INTO THE WAYS OF CASK-CONDITIONED ENLIGHTENMENT

HMM. THIS IS REMINDFUL OF THE GLASS THAT WAS EMBEDDED IN MY FACE AT THE SOMERSET REAL ALE FESTIVAL IN JUNE OF '79

IT WAS AT THE WOODMAN'S ARMS TAVERN IN LANGLEY MARSH. THE LANDLORD'S NAME WAS TONY.

13

Combine the joy of reading the world's dirtiest bongo mags with the pride of owning them in the most luxurious editions.

HAROLD and FRED
THEY MAKE LADIES DEAD

17

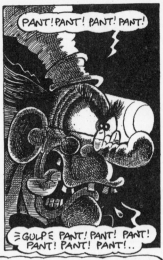

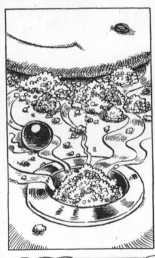

Letterbocks

Star Letter

■ I understand that Dr. Harold Shipman received 15 life sentences for his wicked crimes. I think it is digusting! Why should he be allowed to live 15 times longer than anybody else?

Ian Iro
Ilkley

There's a Letterbox Pen for each letter or tip we print. The sender of the *Star Letter* will recieve, (courtesy of John Brown Publishing's sinister wank mag *Bizzarre*), a fantastic *Cock and Ball Torture Parachute.*

(NB. John Brown Publishing accepts no responsibility for any injuries caused when using letterbox prizes, either pens or genital torture parachutes)

Dead funny

■ Why can't more celebrities die in bizarre circumstances? It's been ages since the last genuinely funny star death. Normal people die in strange ways all the time, but since Rod Hull fell off his roof no celebrity has even tried to peg it in a comedy fashion.

Mark Strongman
e-mail

■ As Professor of Applied Biochemistry at Guys Hospital, I cannot agree with the findings of Prof. Alan Lucas at Great Ormond Street Hospital when he says that *"breast is best"*. I have always been an arse man.

Prof. Stanley Jordan
Guys Hospital

Site for sore brown eyes

■ We have just finished a project to stitch up our flatmate, and would be grateful if you could inform your readership that his hairy backside is plastered all over the net at *www.tomsarse.com*

Tom's Arse Prod.Team
e-mail

* *We visited the site and found it to be a shameful attempt to gain a few cheap laughs at the expense of a drunken man's arse. A link to www.tomsarse.com can be found on the Viz website at www.viz.co.uk*

■ It was reported recently that the largest mass gathering of human beings took place at a religious festival in India on the banks of the Ganges. Amongst the 20 million people was a man who had apparently been holding his hand above his head for forty years. Wouldn't you have thought that someone in a crowd that big would have asked the poor sod what he wanted?

Alf Crust
Wirrel

■ To the fuckwit who scratched *"cunt's"* into the roof of my car: In the unlikely event that the apostrophe was correctly used, the car is actually mine, not yours.

IL
e-mail

■ I am sick and tired of your letters page branding all us truckers as serial killers. For your information, to be classed as a serial killer in the UK, one has to have murdered three or more people (*Gekowski, 1998*). Having only murdered two people (both of whom were female hitch hikers), I feel I am owed an apology.

Jared
Burton upon Trent

Hair today, hair tomorrow

1971   1999

■ Whoever said *Queen* guitarist Brian May has not changed his hairstyle since the seventies is talking nonsesnse. If you compare the two photos *(above)*, one taken in 1971 and the other in 1999, it is perfecrly obvious to anyone that today's style is slightly flatter on the top.

Windsor Holden
Chichester

Headline news

■ Has anyone noticed that all BBC news journalists have long heads (Jeremys Paxman and Vine, Peter Sissons and the sinister Gavin Esler), whilst ITV only hire men with round heads (Trevor McDonald, John Suchet). Channel 5 are not interested in head shape at all and just hire annoying twats instead.

P. Hocker
e-mail

■ My mate's bird likes having her nipples pinched *really hard*. Can any of your readers top that?

MK
Droitwich Spa

* *Well, readers, MK of Droitwich Spa has thrown down the gauntlet. Maybe you've got a mate who's bird likes her arse spanked. Or perhaps your pal's wife loves having her fanny whacked with a cricket bat. Write and let us know at the usual letterbocks address.*

Mug shot

■ "Don't have nightmares" says chirpy Crimewatch UK presenter Nick Ross at the end of each programme. But imagine my horror when watching last month's show I saw that I was one of the muggers featured, caught on CCTV. I am now a complete imsomniac, terrified that I could be arrested at any moment. The dogooders should think twice before making these glib remarks.

Guy
Nottingham

 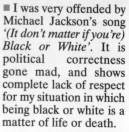

■ I was very offended by Michael Jackson's song *'(It don't matter if you're) Black or White'*. It is political correctness gone mad, and shows complete lack of respect for my situation in which being black or white is a matter of life or death.

A polar bear
Arctica

Cottage pie

■ Here's an estate agent's ad for the best named street in Britain.

MINGE LANE, UPTON-UPON-SEVERN
★ WITHIN LEVEL WALKING DISTANCE of TOWN
★ MATURE DETACHED BUNGALOW
★ REC. HALL, LIVING ROOM, KITCHEN
★ THREE BEDROOMS ... ROOM SEP WC

The road sign is never there, as it is always nicked within days. Perfect for anyone who fancies a little place in the *cuntry.*

Sim Foreman
Fishponds

■ So the Broadcasting Standards Council have decided it is alright for black people to call Her Majesty the Queen a bitch. I am Chinese. Do you think it would be alright if I sent her a turd in the post?

D. Yip
Stafford

■ Whilst flicking through the esteemed pages of Business MK magazine, I spotted *(below)* what must surely be the least convincing Marilyn Monroe lookalike you could ever wish to see. And an incincere smile on the left to boot.

Paul
Newport Pagnell

YOU'RE MORE BEAUTIFUL THAN ANY STAMP IN MY COLLECTION.

PHILATELY WILL GET YOU NOWHERE.

■ Here's a photo of the lasses bogs on the fish quay at North Shields.

How's that for being straight to the point?

Steve Nugent
Gateshead

■ Thought you might like this clipping from the Solihull Times. It gives a whole new outlook on scouting.

Nick Colling
Solihull

＊ *Well spotted, Nick. And well done Jamie Home. Twenty quid is on its way.*

■ Can I be the first to thank the farmers for all the pig, sheep and cow bonfires they have lit up and down the country over the last few weeks. They have certainly brightened up the gloomy winter evenings. How much more of an event for the whole family they would have been, however if they had set off a few chicken fireworks as well.

T. Ball
Exeter

■ Why slaughter and incinerate livestock with foot and mouth disease when they can be redeployed to clear the world's mine fields?

Simon Hollingworth
Norwich

■ I am a burglar, and recently, whilst in the act of nicking a load of stuff from an old widow's house, I tripped on the edge of her rug, spraining my ankle quite badly. I was unable to burgle for three months, so I called that Accident Help Line. They fixed me up with a greedy, manipulative lawyer who got me

Alan Bennet.

■ How about a new photo-spotting competition, "Famous people who look as though they are being taken up the arse"? I'll start the ball rolling with this piccy of Alan Bennett.

Nigel Oakes, Newquay

£50,000, as her carpet should have been better secured to the floor. All that and her pension book too. What wonderful times we live in.

Ben Cormack
Isle of Eigg

Crappy shopper

■ It's amazing what you can buy from your local supermarket these days. Just look at item 3 on this receipt.

```
KWIKSAVE  THE PRIORY
SOMERFIELD STORES LTD
BRISTOL  BS14 0TH

LILT              1.18
MAGAZINE          2.00
DOG EGG           0.95
SUBTOTAL          4.13

CASH             10.00
CHANGE            5.87

NO. OF ITEMS        3

VAT NUMBER  107 4212 12
REC   DATE  TIME  MACH TERM
```

Pam Javelin
Hull

■ They also say that opposites attract. Well how come I'm as ugly as sin and can only attract the kind of birds you have to pay for?

Matthew Wainright
e-mail

■ I have had a fantastic idea for a storyline in Brookside: Jackie is actually a lemon and dykes it off with Shelley whilst Bev and Lindsay

get piped, legs up, by Mick Johno. Oh, and that blonde piece gets it as well. In close up. If the producers are interested, perhaps they could get in contact and I could fill in the details.

David Smith
e-mail

■ After seeing how quickly foot and mouth disease is able to spread through a population, I think it would be sensible to set fire to Princess Margaret now. Her feet are fucked and she can't string two words together. It would be a shame if she were allowed to infect healthy royals like Melons Windsor or that dirty Zara Philips.

J. Dimitri
Wales

TOP TIPS

CINEMA builders. Don't bother installing a front row of seats, nobody ever uses them. Simply start with the second row.

Dave Stuttard
Warrington

MUMS. Keep everyone guessing about whether or not you have just sworn at your children by not saying "...And that's swearing!" after you have just sworn at them.

Guy
Nottingham

BARGAIN sofa hunters. If you missed the DFS December Sale, Double Discount Boxing Day Sale, January Clearance Sale and the February End of Winter Sale, don't worry - the Spring Sale starts in March.

Hanks Martin
Somewhere

EX Blue Peter presenters. Start crying on telly when questioned about the death of your dog. People will never suspect that you used to give him a good hiding with his lead as I once saw you do in Halifax in 1978.

Fat Al White
Wrenthorpe

STRESSED out office bosses. Cover your knackers with tin foil and hit the side of one of them with a hammer. Hey presto! A cheap

yet effective 'Newton's Cradle' type executive toy.

A. Beech
Newcastle

BANKS. Offer people loans when they have plenty of money, and refuse them any help when they haven't got a pot to piss in. And waste millions on expensive headed paper.

David Jones
e-mail

MAKE your steam iron glide effortlessly over your clothes by filling it with vegetable oil instead of water.

Peter Sandlee
London

TWO sprays of Febreeze makes going down on your missus a much more pleasant experience.

M. Johnson
Leigh on Sea

BRITISH comics. Send all your unsold copies of last month's issue to Australia, and call them the 'latest issue'. No one will notice, Christmas is in the middle of February over here.

Texas Pete
Sydney, NSW

FOOL neighbours into thinking your car is automatic by simply selecting reverse momentarily before driving off.

M. Johnson
Leigh on Sea

GRIM GRINS

THERE are quite sinister overtones to this month's crop of insincere smiles.

Health Minister Alan Milburn MP is going to have to try a little harder at smiling if he's going to keep his seat at the next election. "He looks completely scary in this picture from my local paper", writes **Gareth Jones** from

Birmingham who, incidentally offers 'Quality Painting & Decorating (Interiors & Exteriors)'.

Mr. A. Verrall from Epping spotted another bloke who looks like he'd slit your throat for a shilling, David Higgins, Chief of the Bluewater Centre in Kent.

"He's smiling for the camera. What will he look like when he's angry?" mused Mr. Verrall

Steve Johnson from Doncaster sent us a picture of what looks like the man the other two are looking for. "He's supposedly the

manager of our local shopping centre, but look at the eyes. He's a **very** frightened man" writes Steve.

Have you spotted anyone in a local paper or trade gazette paying lip service to a smile? Send them to **'Insincere Smiles'** at the usual Letterbocks address.

We ask...Who is Britain's Most LOVEABLE ROGUE-EST RONNIE?

BIGGS or BARKER

Whether batting for Biggs or backing Barker, we all have our own opinion on who is Britain's most rascally Ronnie. Is it the Great Train Robber Biggs, a latter day Robin Hood who, with his band of 14 merry men, daringly snatched £2.6million from under the very nose of a coshed train driver? Or is it roly-poly funnyman turned antique dealer Barker, who in 1989 cheekily offered an undercover reporter 20 quid for a silver salver valued by Christies at over £1000? *Let's look at the facts...*

SCORE

Coshing — 8 / 5

Big-hearted Biggsy is not a violent man. When he and his fourteen mates set out to rob the overnight Royal Mail train at Cheddington, Bucks, they didn't take any knives or guns to defend themselves. It was only when have-a-go driver Jack Mills tried to make a name for himself by refusing to obey the robbers that roguish Ronnie was left with no option but to bludgeon the 58-year-old into unconsciousness with a sockful of billiard balls.

A low-scoring round for Barker. He has enjoyed a long career in showbusiness, starting out at Aylesbury Rep in 1948. Spotted by David Frost, he got his TV break in 'The Frost Report', before spending most of the 'eighties dressed as a woman singing ribald lyrics to popular tunes. Appearing in sitcoms like 'Porridge' and 'Open All Hours' whilst running his Cotswolds bric a brac shop has left him little time for coshing train drivers.

Escapology — 9 / 4

The prison bars of Wandsworth were no match for cunning convict Ronnie Biggs. After serving a mere 15 months of his 30-year sentence, the wily fox outsmarted his captors, slipping unseen over the wall to freedom. Now back under lock and key at HMP Belmarsh, it can only be a matter of time before the crafty 71-year-old semi-paraplegic shows the screws a clean pair of heels and hightails it back to his luxury Brazilian bolthole.

In 1974, Barker played an habitual criminal, sentenced to five years in Slade Prison for burglary. Looking upon capture and incarceration as occupational hazards, he did his porridge without attempting to escape. The regime at Slade was a fairly relaxed one. During his time inside, Ronnie was never beaten up by the screws, doused with boiling sugary water, fed food containing ground glass or bum-raped in the showers.

Girlfriends — 9 / 7

Ronnie Biggs has always been a glamorous charmer with an eye for the ladies. After his daring escape from Wandsworth Prison in 1965, he flew to exotic Rio, where he bedded a string of sultry Brazilian beauties. Even marriage to the luscious Raimunda de Castro did not curb his playboy lifestyle, and in 1978, he appeared in a Sex Pistols video, eagerly pushing his face into some buxom woman's breasts.

When it comes to the ladies, Barker's life is less than glamorous. There's no bevy of pouting Brazilian-waxed birds for this Ronnie; he's happiest up in the loft, rummaging through his collection of over 70,000 saucy postcards. The closest Barker gets to a real sex session would involve him up a ladder in a brown shop-coat, puffing and blowing whilst trying to push nurse Gladys Emmanuel's enormous arse through an open window.

Speech Impediments — 5 / 9

All lovable rogues have some sort of speech impediment. Think of Terry Thomas with his inability to pronounce the letter 'r' and many more examples of this phenomenon. After three strokes, Biggs's charming cockney patter has been replaced with a series of cheeky grunts accompanied by a rascally string of viscous drool. A good effort.

But anything Biggs can do, Barker can do better! Whether he's shouting for G-G-G-Granville to fee-fer-f-fetch a cloth, or comically "pismronouncing" his "worms", Barker is the king of vocal idiosyncrasies, boasting a wide variety of verbal tics. And they prove no impediment to roguish Ronnie receiving near full marks in this round.

Victims — 2 / 9

The Great Train Robbery, carried out in August 1963, was made all the more dashing and exciting because it was a victimless crime. The money - *worth up to £50 million today* - was destined to be burnt, and train driver Jack Mills was nearing retirement and would probably have died eventually of old age.

From behind the till of his Chipping Norton bric a brac shop, Barker preyed on anyone who came through the door to buy antiques. Old ladies, decorated war heroes, the disabled, children buying presents for their grannies; all were routinely charged MORE for an item than cheeky Ronnie had originally paid.

FINAL SCORE 33

Sorry, but your score is not quite 'Biggs' enough, Ronnie. You're certainly a rogue, but just not quite lovable enough to tip speccy scallywag Barker off top spot.

Lives in Tandem- *More than coincidence???*

Ronnie Biggs and Ronnie Barker have both lived extraordinary lives. But what you may not realise is that their lives share remarkable similarities. Fortean Times editor Paul Sieveking considers these amazing coincidences:

• *Both were born in 1929 on exactly the same day - August 8th. Barker was born just seven weeks later on September 25th.*
• *Both were christened with exactly the same name, spelt identically - Ronnie.*
• *Both started school when they were about 5.*
• *Their best friends (train robber Buster Edwards and Scotch comic Ronnie Corbett) are, to within*

*2 or 3 inches, **exactly** the same height .*
• *Both men celebrated their sixty-fifth birthday in the same year.*
• *Both men's surnames begin with a letter 'B', followed by a vowel.*
• *Followed by **TWO** consonants.*
• *Both stole a train on their 34th birthday. Except Ronnie Barker.*

34 FINAL SCORE

Well done, Ronnie. Out of the two Ronnies, you are the lovable rogue-est. So it's goodnight from you and it's goodnight from him. Goodnight.

BIG MAC & FRY!

"HAVE A NICE last day!" That's what McDonald's staff are saying to their customers at the burger giant's latest branch. For the multi-national fast food corporation has just opened its newest restaurant on Death Row in the Texas State Penitentiary.

For the past 6 years, the jail has executed up to 500 black simpletons a day, with the majority opting for a last meal of Big Mac, fries and a strawberry shake. Quick-thinking McDonald's bosses spotted a gap in the market and the branch is now the fourth busiest in the state.

twenty

Previously, prison Governor Draylon Hogg found that he was sending as many as twenty deputies an hour the seven miles to the

Fast food giants open Death-Row outlet

From our US
Death Row Reporter
Jacqui-Dani Boyles
in LEEDS

nearest drive-thru to buy burgers for condemned inmates.

"This has sure speeded things up," he told CBS reporter Howard Glans. "Now we can have the boys fed, shaved and strapped in the chair before they have a chance to shit their god-damn pants. Yesirree."

Benson

Branch manager John-Bob No-Stars jnr. was adamant that his condemned customers could expect the same level of service as in any other branch of the fast food chain.

"Everyone gets a smile when they enter and a

Dying for a Big Mac - The Texas State Penitentiary with its brand new 'last food' outlet .

'have a nice day' when they leave. And they never have any problems finding a seat. Old Sparky's right on down the hall, first left!" he quipped.

and

And the convicts aren't complaining either.

"I done had me a Happy Meal, cos' they're giving

> "We can have the boys fed, shaved and strapped in the chair before they've had a chance to shit their goddamn pants."

away Animaniacs toys," laughed Jimmy-Ray Joskin, an unemployed farmworker with a mental age of six, wrongly convicted of pretzel theft. It is the fourth time he has been strapped into the electric chair - on the three previous occasions he has been reprieved at the the last minute.

"I got me Yakko, Wakko and Dot. I sure hope I don't get fried before I get me Pinky and the Brain or Slappy Squirrel."

Hedges

Ricky-Bob Robespierre, a 34-year-old retard

sentenced to death for fidgeting during the national anthem at a baseball game has other plans for his final meal. "I'm gonna have me one of them there filet-o-fish thangs. My momma says you have to wait for them and I'll get to live four minutes longer," he said, beaming from ear to ear.

please

Following the success of the Texas Penitentiary branch, McDonalds spokesman Ronald Spunkfelcher hoped to make a killing in prisons right across America. "We've already got plans to have a 24-hour 1 seat restaurant outside the lethal injection chamber in Arkansas State Penitentiary," he said. "Within two years, we want to see those golden arches over every death row in the country. God Bless America."

love

But Spunkfelcher is not the only player trying to corner the last meal market. Already, death-row prisoners in Texas are 10 to a room as cells are demolished to make space for branches of *Taco Bell, Steak 'n' Shake* and *International House of Pancakes.*

Hogg - no-nonsense Redneck Governor yesterday

ARE YOU COMING OUT TONIGHT OR ARE YOU STILL BUSY WORKING?

SORRY, I'VE GOT MASSES TO DO

Final Meals

Name: Bobby-Ray Leonards
Mental age: 8
Crime: Untied shoelaces
Last meal: Big Mac, large fries, donut, Dr. Pepper

Name: Ricky-Bob Moses
Mental age: 3
Crime: TV too loud
Last meal: 6 Chicken McNuggets, regular fries, Coke.

Name: Billy-Bob Berneau
Mental age: 18 months
Crime: None
Last meal: Cheeseburger Happy Meal, McFlurry

THE MISSING LINK of ST. BRIDGET'S

FOR AS LONG AS SHE HAD BEEN AT ST BRIDGET'S SCHOOL, BUNTY CRYSTAL HAD BEEN LONELY

ALL THE OTHER GIRLS SHUNNED HER BECAUSE SHE WAS A MISSING LINK BETWEEN APE AND HUMAN, FORGOTTEN BY TIME

IT WAS THE DAY OF THE FOURTH FORM HOCKEY TRIALS

COME ON GIRLS, SHOW SOME EFFORT

WHEN THE BALL ROLLED NEAR BUNTY SHE BEGAN TO LEAP UP AND DOWN AND SHRIEK EXCITEDLY

YEEK YEEK YEEK

OOH-OOH-OOH AHHH-AHHH!

MISS RANSOME, BUNTY CRYSTAL HAS BROKEN ANOTHER STICK. SHE'S ABSOLUTELY HOPELESS!

PRINCESS DIMONDE TYARA, DAUGHTER OF A WEALTHY BAILIFF, REGARDED BUNTY HAUGHTILY

WE DON'T WANT HER ON OUR TEAM

WHY, SHE HAS BARELY EVOLVED FURTHER THAN A LOWLY PRIMATE

CRIMSON WITH SHAME, BUNTY SLOWLY KNUCKLED HER WAY OFF THE PITCH

IN THE SCHOOL DINING HALL THE PRE-NEANDERTHAL SCHOOLGIRL ATE ALONE AS USUAL

EE-EE-EE

AA-AA-AA

JUST THEN PRINCESS DIMONDE WALKED BY

TSK! SEE HOW BUNTY DEFECATES INTO HER HAND AND THROWS IT ALL OVER THE ROOM

HOW PRIMITIVE! WE STOPPED DOING THAT 200,000 YEARS AGO!

WITH THEIR CRUEL JIBES ECHOING IN HER EARS, BUNTY RUSHED OUT OF THE DINING HALL TEARFULLY

ALL AFTERNOON BUNTY SWUNG FORLORNLY FROM A TREE, PICKING HER ANUS

OO-OO-OO

WOULD SHE NEVER BE ACCEPTED BY HER CLASSMATES AT ST. BRIDGETS?

SUDDENLY SHE HEARD A CRY FOR HELP BELOW — PRINCESS DIMONDE TYARA WAS BEING KIDNAPPED!

GET INTO THE CAR, YOUNG LADY

YOUR FATHER WILL PAY US A GOOD RANSOM FOR YOU

WITHOUT A SECOND THOUGHT BUNTY LEAPT ONTO THE BONNET OF THE KIDNAPPERS' CAR

YEEK! YEEK! YEEK!

WHAT ON EARTH...?!

ABANDON KIDNAPPING! THAT CRAZY APE HAS SLIGHTLY BENT THE WINDSCREEN WIPER!

AND IT'S PULLING THE RUBBER TRIM OFF THE WINDOWS! RUN FOR IT!

OH BUNTY, YOU SAVED ME FROM BEING KIDNAPPED

CAN YOU EVER FORGIVE ME FOR BEING SO HORRID TO YOU?

THAT NIGHT IN THE DORMITORY, PRINCESS DIMONDE HELD A CELEBRATORY FEAST

POP

THREE CHEERS FOR BUNTY, THE BEST MISSING LINK IN THE WHOLE WORLD

HIP HIP - HOORAY!

28

HOPE SPRINGS ETERNAL

Comic Bob lingers a while on the road to Heaven

VETERAN comedian Bob Hope was celebrating with friends last night as his final days entered their *THIRD* sucessive year. Family and friends of the 98-year-old Hollywood star have been holding a round-the-clock bedside vigil since he began fading fast in June 1999.

Hope's runaway deathbed run has smashed all records. The previous longest demise was set by Frank Sinatra, who spent a marathon two and a half years facing his final curtain. "I knew that Bob's death would be a wow, but I never dreamed it would be such a blockbuster," said his long time friend and agent Hyman Prepuce.

trooper

And as crowds flock to pay their last respects, the demise shows no sign of coming to an end. "Bob's a real trooper. His heartbeat is weak and erratic, his breathing shallow and laboured, his hearing and eyesight have left him. But this death is gonna run and run."

In fact audiences have risen since January, after rumours that Bob's life would close at the end of the month.

glue

Tickets to the deathbed vigil are changing hands for over $1000 each. A tout in Rancho Mirage,

> *"His heartbeat is weak and erratic, his breathing is shallow and laboured. This death is gonna run and run!"*

By our Hollywood Correspondent
Fanny Batter

Hope's luxury mansion in Bel Air, where his one man death show is packing them in.

California told us: "This is Tinsel Town's 'must see' demise of the year. It seems like everyone wants to see Bob knocking on death's door."

man

One Beverly Hills friend said this was the best bereavements ever to hit Hollywood: "I've seen Bob on his deathbed 29 times already, and I'm going again to the matinee on Saturday."

natural

Hyman Prepuce refused to confirm that Bob may spend a season passing away on Broadway.

"It's a little early to say yet, but nothing is ruled out." he told reporters.

annuation

"There's even been talks about a world tour with Bob passing away for a few months in London's West End. Let's just wait and see."

'Hats Off' to Bridlington!

Cap-Happy Brid Brim-full o' Titfers

'Hat's the way to do it!' A typical Bridlington scene ironically without any hats and (above) Mayor Oyster Jackanory, also ironically without a hat neither.

'IF YOU want to get ahead, get a hat'... *or go to Bridlington!* For the popular seaside resort has been voted 'Hat Capital of East Yorkshire' by *East Yorkshire Milliner* magazine.

Editor Ron Gubba said: "There are 2.8 hats per head of population in Bridlington, compared to 2.76 throughout the rest of the region. It may be something in the water, but Bridlingtoners are mad as hatters for their hats!"

The town's Lord Mayor, Mr. Oyster Jackanory was delighted with the findings. "It's another pat on the head, or rather *hat* on the head, for Bridlington", he quipped.

"I'd take my hat off to the townsfolk, only it's been eaten by a goat."

–Reuters

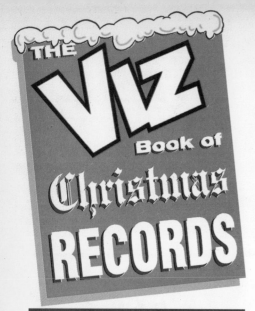

THE Viz BOOK OF Christmas RECORDS

Eating

Date discrepancy

The record for the biggest disparity between dates eaten on Christmas day versus the rest of the year is held by Phillip Runcorn (GB) of Derby. Between 8.30 am and 11.30 pm on 25th Dec 1998, he consumed a total of *23.456 Kg* (51lb 12½oz) of 'Eat Me' dates, despite not particularly liking them. During the previous 364 days he had eaten half a date weighing 7gm (0.247oz) whilst at his brother's wedding, an annual discrepancy of *23.449kg* or 335214.28%.

Presents

Longest gift-related huff

On November 29th 1968, Margaret Pierce of Gateshead (GB), told her husband Ron not to get her anything that year for Christmas. When on Christmas morning she found that he hadn't, she embarked upon a huff which as of Nov 14th 2001 has lasted for 11981 days. During this time man landed on the Moon, the Berlin wall has been torn down and a third world war has begun. Meanwhile, Mrs Pierce has sat with her arms folded, pretending to watch the telly and affecting not to hear her husband.

Most socks

On Christmas day 1996, Mr Brigham Osmond, a polygamous Mormon of Salt Lake City, Utah (US) received 847 pairs of socks from his ten wives, 84 children and 753 grandchildren. The following year, thanks to the addition of 2 more wives, six more children, 56 grandchildren and a great grandchild, he received 912 bottles of Pagan Man aftershave.

Children

Earliest wake-up

Henry and James Mongomery of Basildon (GB) were so excited about opening their presents from Santa on Christmas Day 1999, that they woke up at 2.33 am on October 25th 1998. Their bleary-eyed father John told them to go back to bed, as there were still 14 months to go.

Least convincing Santa

In December 1998, in the Grotto at Claire's Department Store in Llandudno (GB), Dafydd Postgate managed to fool only three children, two of whom were blind, that he was

> **Most socks ● Ho! Ho! Hose!** Brigham Osmond opens his last present on Christmas morning.

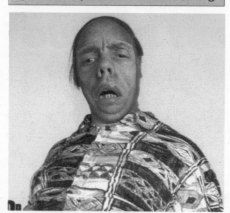

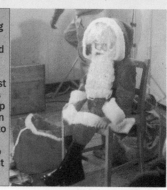

Least convincing Santa ● 12 year-old Dafydd Postgate fools almost no one as he takes up his position in the grotto at his Llandudno department store

the real Santa Claus. Postgate, the manager's 12-year-old son was ordered to put on a cotton wool beard after all staff had refused. His high-pitched Ho! Ho! Ho's did little to convince the 687 children who visited the grotto that year, many of whom left in tears. Postgate estimated that he had had his beard pulled off over 500 times by irate toddlers.

Trees

Most Christmas trees behind shed

On January 6th 1946, Ernest Sands of Northampton (GB) put his Christmas tree behind the garden shed, intending to take it to the municipal tip at that weekend. At the time of writing, Mr. Sands has 56 similar trees behind the shed, which he has had to extend five times to accommodate them. He intends to definitely take them to the tip this year.

Parties

Arse photocopying

The record for the most photocopying of arses at an office Christmas party is held by the staff of Eversheds Solicitors in Newcastle upon Tyne (UK). On Dec 23rd 1987 a total of *6938* A3 buttock copies were produced on a standard Sharp SF2035 copier. During the 4-hour party, 14 reams of paper were used, the toner cartridges were changed 8 times and the service engineer was called out twice.

Christmas Day TV Choice
Your essential guide to what's on TV this Christmas...

9.00 BBC 2: I Love Scraping the Bottom of the Barrel Assorted B-list celebrities pretend to remember their childhood in precise detail whilst sitting in front of a coloured backdrop. **9.00 ITV: Branching Out** Ross Kemp stars as Robson Thaw, an unconventional tree surgeon who sometimes bends the rules but always gets results. **9.30 ITV: The Ross Kemp Story** Robson Green stars as Ross Kemp in the true life story of an unconventional actor who sometimes bends the rules but always gets results. **10.00 BBC 2: I Love Staurt Maconie's Opinions.** Assorted fame hungry K-list media tarts reminisce about some of Stuart Maconie's most memorable opinions on everything from Hula Hoops and Space Hoppers to Clackers and Chopper bikes. **11.30 ITV: Ross Kemp vehicle** Another fucking programme starring Ross Kemp. Details to be confirmed. **12.00 C4: Escape From Cardiff** Claudia Winkleman introduces an exciting adventure game in which two teams of whooping lycra-clad twats are given a week to attempt to get out of The Welsh capital and reach civilsation. **1.00 ITV: Robson Green, QC** Legal drama, starring

Ross Kemp as John Thaw, an unconventional police astrologer who sometimes bends the rules but always gets results. **1.00 BBC 2: I Love Doing These Sorts of Programmes.** Desperate attention-seeking T-list celebrities reminisce about their favourite appearances on these sorts of programmes. **1.30 BBC 1: Christmas Pro-Celebrity Golf** Bruce Forsyth, Jimmy Tarbuck and Kenny Lynch play a round of golf with three prostitutes. Introduced by Peter Allis. **2.00 ITV: The weather** with Ross Kemp **3.00 ITV: The Queens Christmas message** The traditional Christmast Day broadcast to the commonwealth, starring Ross Kemp as Elizabeth Windsor, the unconventional monarch who sometimes bends the rules but always gets results. **3.30 BBC 2: I Love Not Decided at Time of Going to Press.** Tragic W-list nonentities and Jamie Theakston reminisce about something which had not been decided at time of going to press. **4.00 Carlton Food Network: Cooking for One** Anthea Turner cooks a Stilton cheese souffle with chick pea couscous whilst a single viewer watches. **6.00 ITV: Kemp it in the Family** Hilarious sitcom by Robson Green. Ross and Martin

Kemp play Martin and Ross Kemp, two divorced brothers who marry each other's ex-wives, played by Amanda Burton and John Thaw. This week, Ross pretends he has forgotten his anniversary, but Martin has secretly planned a surprise party! **9.00 ITV: Search for a Kemp** It's down to the last two finalists, Martin and Ross. Who will impress the judges the most and win 8 badly-written drama series? On the panel are John Thaw, Amanda Burton, Robson Green, Sarah Lancashire and Ross Kemp. **10.00 ITV: What the Kemps Did for Us** Adam Hart-Davis looks at the contributions to civilization made by the Kemps, Ross and Martin. This week, bad acting in hoarse voices. **10.30 ITV: Morse** John Thaw plays Ken Morse, an unconventional rostrum cameraman who sometimes bends the rules but always gets results. **11.00 ITV: The Kemps - A Warning from History** Harrowing documentary outlining the circumstances that allowed two unversatile cockney baddy actors to seize power of an entire television network. Narrated by Ross Kemp. **12.30 ITV: Carry On Kemping** Late night saucy fun, starring Sid James as Ross Kemp and Jack Douglas as Martin Kemp.

WIG WATCH

Sender: J. Harris, Welwyn Garden City

Sender: Graham Doyle, Liverpool

syrups@viz.co.uk

> HOW ABOUT THESE?
>
> I'M NOT SURE. I'D BESTTRY THE SIZE HUNDRED AND FORTY TWO AND A HALFS.

Jack Black
& his dog Silver
in the
Milky Mystery

The Whitsun holidays were here once more, and Jack had come to stay with Aunt Meg at her picturesque Cumbrian dairy farm, in the heart of the Kent Weald...

HERE'S YOUR PUDDING JACK.

YUM! MY ABSOLUTE FAVOURITE! RHUBARB WITH LASHINGS OF CUSTARD!

I'M SORRY JACK. WE'VE NO CUSTARD. YOU'LL HAVE TO HAVE IT WITH WATER.

NO CUSTARD!? WHYEVER NOT?

I'M AFRAID THERE'S NO MILK. OUR WHOLE HERD WAS DESTROYED ON EEC ORDERS, AS A SAFEGUARD AGAINST FOOT AND MOUTH.

WHAT!? UNCLE BOB'S PRIZE HERD OF JERSEYS. DAISY, BUTTERCUP, KEITH AND ALL THE REST OF THEM?

I'M AFRAID SO JACK. UP IN SMOKE, EVERY LAST ONE.

BOB WAS SO UPSET HE TOOK HIS OWN LIFE.

UNCLE BOB DEAD AND NO CUSTARD FOR MY RHUBARB! DRAT THOSE FRENCHIES AND THEIR SILLY LAWS!

NEVER MIND, JACK. THERE'S A CIRCUS VISITING THE VILLAGE. WHY DON'T YOU AND YOUR DOG SILVER POP ALONG. IT MIGHT HELP TAKE YOUR MIND OFF THE CUSTARD.

YES AUNT MEG. I THINK WE WILL.

The boy detective and his canine companion soon arrived at the village green, where the giant circus tent had been erected.

I HOPE IT'S A PROPER CIRCUS WITH DANCING ELEPHANTS AND TIGERS BEING MADE TO JUMP THROUGH FIREY HOOPS.

CIRCUS

WOOF!

SORRY, SONNY. TODAY'S PERFORMANCE HAS BEEN CANCELLED. SOMEBODY BROKE IN LAST NIGHT AND STOLE ALL MY DWARVES OUT OF THEIR CAGE.

GASP!

PC BROWN! WHAT ON EARTH'S GOING ON?

IT'S THE RUMMEST CASE I'VE EVER COME ACROSS, YOUNG JACK. A DOZEN DWARVES STOLEN, AND THE ONLY CLUE WE CAN FIND IS THIS SAFETY PIN, WHICH WAS USED TO PICK THE PADLOCK.

HMMMM...

Later, over tea, Jack explained to his aunt what had happened...

...AND NOBODY HAS ANY IDEA WHO DID IT!

THAT IS A QUEER DO, AND NO MISTAKE. ANYWAY, HAVE A NICE BOWL OF MY HOME-MADE APPLE PIE...WITH SOME GRAVY.

KNOCK! KNOCK!

I WONDER WHO THAT COULD BE.

I YOST CALLING FOR SEE IF YOU NEEDING MILK. I ARE HAB SO MANY PINTS. TASTY, VERY GOOD. VERY GOOD.

NO THANK-YOU, MR KADIJAVIC. I'M NOT PAYING YOUR PRICES, YOU DIRTY FOREIGN ROB-DOG.

WHO WAS THAT?

THAT WAS MR KADIJAVIC. HE'S CASHING IN ON THE MILK SHORTAGE BY CHARGING A PENNY EXTRA PER PINT, THE THEIVING ARAB.

THE CHEATING TURK. TRYING TO JEW YOU OVER THE MILK.

GRRR! GLACK GASTARD!

Jack went to bed after a mug of Horlicks made with vinegar. He and Silver tossed and turned all night with troubled dreams...

DWARF URINE ON YOUR TOFFEE PUDDING, JACK?

WE MUST SLAUGHTER YOUR DOG SILVER, IMMEDIATLICH!

OUI, MONSIEUR JACK. HE IS NOT MEETING OUR EURO STANDARDS!

LEAVE HIM ALONE! I WANT PROPER CUSTARD!

HA-HA-HA-HA! I GOT LOTS MILK! THIRTY FIVE PENCE FOR BOTTLE! YOU WANT, YOU PAY! HEH-HEH!

WHAT AN AWFUL DREAM!

Jack and Silver were unable to get back to sleep, and went into the garden for some fresh air just as dawn was breaking...

WOOF!

WHAT IS IT, LAD? WHAT HAVE YOU FOUND?

IT'S A NAPPY. THAT CROOKED MILKMAN MUST OF DROPPED IT WHEN HE CALLED LAST NIGHT.

BUT WHY WOULD A MILKMAN BE CARRYING A NAPPY? COME ON SILVER... THERE'S DETECTIVE WORK TO BE DONE.

33

Jack and Silver made their way into the village, and soon found what they were looking for...

SOMEHOW, WE'VE GOT TO GET INTO KADIJAVIC'S DAIRY.

RIGHT, LAD. YOU KEEP HIM BUSY WHILST I HIDE IN HIS FLOAT.

L. KADIJAVIC

DALEY FRESH MILK

The wily hound quickly began distracting the milkman by copulating with his leg...

AN ONION SACK!? ON A MILK FLOAT? THE PLOT THICKENS.

NO! FEELTHY ANIMAL! STOBBIT! PUT AWAY YOUR LEEPSTICK! YOU IS DIRTY DOG!

YAR! IF LJUBOMIR HAD HIS GUN HE SHOOT YOUR KNACKERS OFF! BANG BANG BLADDY QUICK!

The milkman was nearing the end of his rounds, and it wasn't long before Jack found himself being driven through the heavily-guarded gates of Kadijavic's dairy...

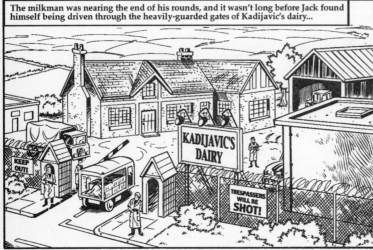

KADIJAVIC'S DAIRY

KEEP OUT!

TRESPASSERS WILL BE SHOT!

Once inside the compound, Jack lost no time in shinning up the drainpipe to the diary roof...

NOW TO FIND OUT WHAT'S GOING ON.

GREAT SCOTT! SO THAT'S WHERE THE CRAFTY CROAT'S GETTING HIS MILK. WAIT TILL I TELL PC BROWN ABOUT THIS!

Minutes later, Jack interrupted the policeman's breakfast...

PC BROWN! PC BROWN! HUNDREDS OF REFUGEES! HE DROPPED A SAFETY PIN AND THERE'S NO CUSTARD! I WAS ON THE ROOF OF THE DAIRY AND KADIJAVIC PICKED THE LOCK WITH A LOAD OF ONIONS AND THAT'S WHY HE'S GOT MILK ONLY IT'S THIRTY FIVE PEE! AND...AND...

WHOA THERE, YOUNG FELLOW-ME-LAD. LET'S START AT THE BEGINNING, SHALL WE?

Once he heard Jack's story, the bobby lost no time in tooling up, and setting off for the dairy...

TAKE THAT! YOU SCHEMING SERB!

AHCTUNG! ICH IST JACK SCHWARZ UND ZER HUND, ZIL...AIEEEEE!

QUICK, PC BROWN! THROUGH HERE!

NO ENTRY!

BLESS MY SOUL, YOU WERE RIGHT, JACK. KADIJAVIC HAS CORNERED THE MARKETIN ILLEGAL ASYLUM SEEKER LADIES, AND HE'S BEEN FARMING THEM FOR THEIR BOOSIE-MILK.

LOOK OUT, PC BROWN! HE'S TRYING TO SURRENDER!

BANG!

GOOD SHOT! RIGHT IN THE FACE!

It wasn't long before reinforcements arrived to take the topless lady refugees into custody...

THIS IS ALL VERY WELL, JACK. BUT THERE'S STILL ONE THING I DON'T UNDERSTAND.

WHAT'S THAT?

WHERE DO THE DWARVES, NAPPIES AND ONIONS FIT IN?

BOO-HOO! BOO-HOO! WAH!

WHAT THE...?

KADIJAVIC STOLE THE DWARVES AND DRESSED THEM AS BABIES. HE USED THE ONIONS TO MAKE THEM CRY AND THEN PARADED THEM ROUND THE DAIRY...

...THE SIGHT AND SOUND OF CRYING BABIES ENCOURAGED THE ILLEGAL IMMIGRANTS TO LACTATE, INCREASING HIS MILK YIELD.

WHAT'S GOING TO HAPPEN NOW?

WELL, THE ILLEGAL ALIEN WOMEN WILL BE SENT BACK TO THEIR OWN COUNTRY...

...AND FURTHER!

...TO BE DEALT WITH BY THE PROPER AUTHORITIES...

...AS FOR THE DWARVES...

Later...

IT WAS SO NICE OF PC BROWN TO LET YOU KEEP THEM, JACK.

YES. MY OWN MINIATURE CIRCUS!

ALLEZ-OOP!

The End

BIFFA BACON

BIFFA IS DOING A PARACHUTE JUMP FOR CHARITY...

RIGHT, BIFFA. JUMP OUT THE PLANE AND COUNT TO FOUR BEFORE PULLING THE RIPCORD.

ONE THOOSAND! TWO THOOSAND! THREE THOOSAND! FAWA THOOSAND!

PULL!

EH!?

THWACK!

HEH-HEH!

COO! NOO I'LL HEV TO URPEN ME EMERGENCY PARACHUTE!

YANK!

BANG! BANG! BANG! BANG!

OOYAH!

HAPPY LANDINGS, BIFFA SON!

THE FUCKIN' PAIR O' FUCKIN' CUNTS.

LATER... DING DONG!

WHO THE FUCKS THAT, FATHA?

IT'S BIFFA. HE'S COME FOR 'IS BIT SPONSAH MONEY.

PEEPING TOM THE TANK ENGINE

1   *"Toot toot!"* whistled Tom as he chugged happily into town, proudly pulling his two shiny coaches - one for just passengers, and one for passengers, their luggage and the guard.

2   But look! What did Tom spy in the window? Why, it was Sir Toppsan Fingers's wife Shelley with the smashing tits - and *she was getting her kit off!*

3   *"Phwoaar!"* said Tom. "Fuck me - I'll have a squint at that! And he hurried to her window-sill as quietly as he could. *"Chuffa-chuffa-chuffa! CHUFFA! CHUFFA! CHUFFA! CHUFFA!"*

4   *"Bah!"* shouted Sir Toppsan Fingers. "You've been getting steamed up about my missus's churns again, haven't you?" Tom was in disgrace. "I'll *never* do it again", he whistled sadly.

Next Week: Tom falls off the viaduct into the canal when he cops an eyeful of Lady Fingers sunbathing topless in the back garden.

The CURSE of TUTANKHAMUN

LUXOR, NOVEMBER 26th 1922. HOWARD CARTER AND LORD CARNARVON HAVE FINALLY CHANCED UPON THE TOMB OF TUTANKHAMUN

AT LAST! THE TOMB OF TUTANKHAMUN. MY 30 YEAR SEARCH IS ENDED.

HURRAH!

LOOK, CARNARVON... HIEROGLYPHS!

WHAT DO THEY SAY, CARTER?

THEY SAY "BEWARE ALL YOU WHO ENTER HERE, AND SUFFER MY CURSE".

"PCHAW!" WHAT BALLDERDASH AND POPPYCOCK!

WHAT CAN YOU SEE, CARTER?

THERE ARE WONDERFUL TREASURES HERE, BUT IT'S ALL STREWN ABOUT AS IF THE TOMB HAS BEEN ROBBED AT SOME TIME.

THE PLACE IS IN A TERRIBLE MESS.

TERRIBLE MESS? TERRIBLE MESS?!

I'D LIKE TO SEE YOU KEEP THIS PLACE TIDY WITHOUT ANY HELP. YOU DON'T KNOW WHAT IT'S LIKE, STUCK DOWN HERE DEAD FOR 4000 YEARS.

HEY. DON'T SHOUT AT US. WE DIDN'T MAKE THE MESS!

TAKE NO NOTICE CARNARVON. IT'S JUST A RAG RAGE. HE'LL CALM DOWN IN A MINUTE.

HOW DARE YOU! I AM CALM! I'M PERFECTLY CALM! HOW DARE YOU SAY I'M NOT CALM!!

ERM... COME ALONG. CALM DOWN OLD THING.

WE'LL COME BACK NEXT WEEK WHEN THE PAINTERS HAVE GONE.

GOOD IDEA.

LEW STRINGER. GFD. VIZ 107

37

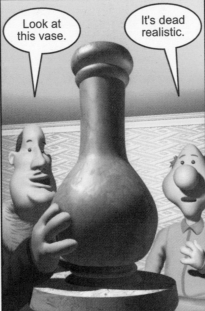

CONTINUED NEXT PAGE...

Government split as Minister slips up on official statements

YES, we have no Nazi Bananas!

THE GOVERNMENT Minister for Fruit, Angela Spratt, was yesterday facing calls for her resignation after a local newspaper found evidence that Nazi bananas are being grown in Oxfordshire.

Dick Gleet, environment correspondent of the Banbury Cake, posed as a scarecrow to gain access to a farm in Burford where he found Nazi bananas being grown in a field. Questions were asked in parliament after pictures of the fruit appeared in his paper.

U-turn

"It's a typical government U-turn," Gleet told us. "In March 2000, Mrs Spratt told the House of Commons that under no circumstances would National Socialist fruit or vegetables be grown in this country. Yet here we are less than a year later, and they're being cultivated right on our doorstep."

U-bend

But the minister was adamant that nothing had changed: "The govern-ment's stance remains the same," she lied to reporters.

S-bend

"What I actually said was that these products would never be grown *commercially* in this country. The Nazi bananas found by Mr Gleet were being grown experimentally, and would never have entered the food chain."

S-Club 7

However, Tesco's in Truro openly admitted that Nazi bananas were on sale. "They're on special offer," said supermarket manager Foreskin Trevithick. "We've got Nazi 'nanas, peaches and mangos, organic Stalinist apples and Italian fascist pears. We even had some Khmer Rouge pineapples but they sold out straight away."

by our GM Foods Correspondent
Fanny Discharge

We called the Ministry of Fruit for a statement, but a spokesman told us: "I'm afraid the minister is unavailable for comment as her pants are on fire."

Gleet (right) in the scare-crow disguised used to enter the banana field

Spratt's Nazi Banana Statements in FULL

"I CAN assure the house that under no circumstances will nazi bananas be grown in this country. This government have never, do not, and never will tolerate the cultivation of Nazi crops in Britain."

Angela Spratt MP, Parliament, March 8th 2000. (Hansard)

"I HAVE not said Nazi bananas will never be grown in this country. I have always maintained that experimental crops of Nazi fruit may need to be grown from time to time, but that these will never be sold for public consumption."

Angela Spratt MP, on Radio 4's Today programme, February 2nd, 2001

Letterbocks

write to us at
Letterbocks, Viz Comic, PO Box 1PT,
Newcastle upon Tyne, NE99 1PT

E-mail
toptips@
letterbocks
.com

Mickey Rooney is still full of spunk

Star Letter

MY GRANDAD was the best drummer who ever lived, despite only having biscuit tins for a drum kit and two rolling pins for sticks. Although he had a poor sense of timing and rhythm, he compensated with a heavy handed playing style and practised enthusiastically for 18 hours a day. My Nan didn't appreciate his skills, however, and after 50 years of pounding, she stabbed him in the throat in 1985.

Darren Jarvis, e-mail

■ NO WONDER there is so much voter apathy. Politicians ask us to vote with our feet, then place the ballot box high on a table in the voting booth. With that prospect in mind, no wonder people choose to stay at home.

Ade Smith
Basingstoke

On the knocker

■ I WONDER if I could use your letters page to warn women about a scam that is going on. If a man comes to your door and asks to look at your tits, claiming to be doing a survey, do not show him your tits. I fell for this the other day, and it was only later I discovered that there was no survey, he was only trying to see my tits.

B. Harrison
e-mail

■ I WISH disabled people would stop moaning on about there being no access to public buildings. They get to sit in their wheelchairs whilst being carried up and down large flights of stairs - the rest of us have to walk.

W. Walker
Norwich

■ I RECENTLY watched Comic Relief's Red Nose Day on TV and was horrified by some of the humour. Frankly, I found the comedy shorts on Africa to be in rather poor taste. Call me old-fashioned but my idea of something funny is a man falling down a hole, or being hit in the face with a custard pie.

Ben Cormack
Isle of Eigg

■ ENCLOSED is a photo of my version of the Milliennium Dome which I built whilst holidaying in the Canary Islands. It cost a few million quid less than the actual dome, but proved to be just as interesting.

Giles Barton
London

■ I RECENTLY wrote to Letterbocks (signed Mad Dog) and would ask that my letter be destroyed. It is not funny and would cause distress to the relatives of the bereaved. I cannot explain why I thought it funny and am ashamed I did.

Mad Dog
London

Ab Fab Bag

■ JANE Horrocks was in front of me in the post office queue in Twickenham last week. I noticed her handbag contained the contraceptive pill and a fag lighter in the shape of a penis. And she also has a bob or two as she was sending birthday cards to Norwich by registered post. Any other readers know the contents of celebrity handbags?

Helen Smith
Strawberry Hill

* Have you ever peeped inside a star's handbag? Did you see anything embarrassing or illegal? Or perhaps you were the mystery recipient of that Norwich-bound birthday card. Write and let us know.

■ I WAS reading Razzle this morning and I couldn't help thinking that if these were the readers' wives, no wonder they read periodicals with an artistic focus on knockers and twats. Didn't stop me throwing some dripping over them, though.

Mike Barman
e-mail

■ I THOUGHT your readers would be amused by the caption printed under this picture of quasi-troll Mickey Rooney in an American newspaper. I'm guessing that being short, ugly, almost dead and unable to tug his forever flaccid little cock would account for the build-up of jizz.

Reed Kirk Rahlmann
San Francisco

■ CAN I just inform your more ignorant readers that not all lorry drivers are murderers. Some of them are just rapists.

Timbo
Hull

■ CAN anyone tell me the basis upon which the Queen's Birthday and New Year's Honours are awarded? Tory politician Norman Lamont is awarded a peerage and Eddie George, governor of the Bank of England is knighted. It seems farcical. Frank Bruno

could floor both of them with one punch, and he only gets an OBE.

P. Geils
Oldham

■ I WONDER if you might publish this picture of a Quaver which I drew and then

ate while I was bored at work. I can also do Hula-Hoops.

Arthur
Wakefield

ARE YOU COMING FOR A DRINK IN THE SALOON?

UNIVERSAL STUDIOS

SALOON

SORRY, ITS REALLY NOT MY SCENE

Thyme for a wee

■ WHILST cleaning Jamie Oliver's windows the other day, I pissed in his window box with herbs in. Have any of your other readers done spiteful things to celebrities?

OTG
Herts

■ YOU'LL never guess what happened to me. I travelled on holiday to Holland and forgot to take my coat - and it rained every day for a fortnight! Luckily I had taken a spare one along with me.

J. Rackham
Oxford

■ NICE to hear about nipple twisting pleasure (MK's bird, page 20). My boyfriend loves it when I give his nudger a Chinese Burn. He just begs for more, the little slag.

Cathy
Stockport

■ NO WONDER the BBC has been accused of dumbing down when it continues to allow basic grammatical errors. With just two contestants remaining, hairy-faced boiler Anne Robinson should be playing 'The Weaker Link' - every schoolboy knows that one.

Juan Kerr
Sileby

■ ERM... does anyone know if foot and mouth can be transmitted sexually? I have a friend who would like to know.

Al
e-mail

■ VANESSA Feltz has gone on record saying that being slim hasn't brought her happiness. Slim? Now, hold on. She may have lost a stone or two, but there are varying degrees of lardiness and she's still just one step behind a pot-bellied pig in my opinion.

L. Henman
e-mail

■ THEY say that Jennifer Lopez is sexy because she's got a big arse. Well if that's the case, then my girlfriend is at least twice as sexy as her.

Richard Harrison
Gwynedd

■ WHY is it every time I take a chimpanzee into my house, it puts fucking butter in my shoe or something? I've a good mind to stop letting chimps into my house.

Alan Mogarry
e-mail

■ I HAVE just received a pen from Shelter (A Charity for the Homeless). It's very kind of them, but I have got dozens of pens and have absolutely no need for another one. Surely they would have been better spending the money on buying a box for a person with homelessness to live in.

Mark Luty
e-mail

■ WHY IS it when nutters hear voices, they are always telling them to go out and kill women? Why don't they ever tell them to do something a little less extreme, like wash the car or give the missus a hand with the ironing?

M. Robson
Northumberland

TOP TIPS

MEN. Attract loads of gorgeous women in the most remote locations by simply releasing a foul-smelling fart. They will appear as if by magic at this inopportune time.

Steve Morris, Cheshire

WOMEN. Why take two bottles into the shower when you can take about a dozen, cluttering up the shelf so there is no room for the single bottle of all over shampoo that we seem to be able to manage perfectly well with? For fuck's sake.

Iain Purdie, Bradford

EARN big money by displaying a "How's My Driving?" sign on your car, along with an 0906 number (£1.50 per minute) which you can aquire through BT. Then simply drive around town like a complete arsehole.

Jim, Lancaster

CASH strapped police forces. The average police woman's uniform costs around £250. But Ann Summers' shops do a wipe-clean one for under twenty. So save money and improve public relations in one stroke.

W. Walker, e-mail

CONVINCE your wife that she's 'followed through' during the night by slipping a chocolate button between the cheeks of her arse as she sleeps.

Ray Devereaux, Bodmin

WOMEN travel writers. Get paid a fortune to travel somewhere wonderful and exotic and then submit the usual article about about how useful a sarong is.

Dave Stuttard, e-mail

A CIGARETTE but placed beneath a Band-Aid makes a cheap nicotine patch.

Scott & Stu, e-mail

SUPERMARKETS. Save money on printing by labelling your 'Economy' goods 'Shit' instead.

Cat & Trev, Newcastle

DON'T waste money buying Lo-salt. Normal salt is the same height and twice as tasty.

J. Reichelt, e-mail

WHEN asked if you have any questions at a job interview, increase your chances of getting the job by asking the interviewer, or the whole panel in turn where they get their hair cut.

James James, e-mail

BIG Brother winners. After having every fart, shit and piss broadcast to the nation, keep what little dignity you have left by not releasing a piss-poor single at Christmas.

Treeve Menear, Penzance

SEX offenders with a taste for elderly ladies. Lure your victims into your car with the promise of medicine and slippers.

D. Smith, e-mail

TAXI drivers. Remove the bulbs from your indicators in case you momentarilly forget what you do for a living and inadvertantly signal.

Aiden, e-mail

DIY enthusiasts. Make your approach more professional by starting 3 days late, wearing ill fitting trousers and shaking your head at regular intervals

J. O'Reilly, Stockport

DRIVERS. Avoid being nicked by the new 'average speed' blue cameras by driving at 90mph for two minutes between them, them stopping for a spliff.

Ray Wilson, e-mail

MAKERS of the Gillette Mach 3 razor. Save money by putting the blade that shaves the closest at the front and forgetting about the other two.

Orbish, e-mail

SAVE 40p a week by just giving 60p to a big issue vendor instead of buying the magazine.

Guy Morris, e-mail

A SERIES of quiet burps in your sleeping wife's ear will ensure she has pleasant dreams about burps. Similar results can be achieved with farts.

Kelly, Ulsan

SADO-Masochists. Don't waste money on dominatrix prostitutes. Simply travel on a Virgin train at 5pm on a Friday. Discomfort, degradation, real danger and verbal abuse from specialists in uniform for a fraction of what you would spend in Marylebone.

Ishmael Skyes, London

Cooper's Fist goes under Hammer

by our sports correspondant Ronald Pianno

Ex-champ hopes right hook lands knockout price!

BOXING legend Sir Henry Cooper is to auction off his right hand in an attempt to stave off bankruptcy.

The troubled ex-heavyweight has already been forced to sell his Lonsdale belts and take part in a series of embarassing adverts for roofing felt after losing all his money in the Lloyds collapse. Selling off one of his fists is seen as a desperate move.

price

Michael de Wankman, director of sports memorabilia at Sotheby's Auctioneers was confident that the famous 'Henry's Hammer' would fetch a good price.

van gogh

"You must remember this is the hand that knocked the then Cassius Clay to the floor in 1963. There are very few of those hands in existence, so we've set a high reserve of £250" he told reporters.

van dyke

"We are hoping for a British buyer who will allow the hand to stay on Mr. Cooper's wrist, but

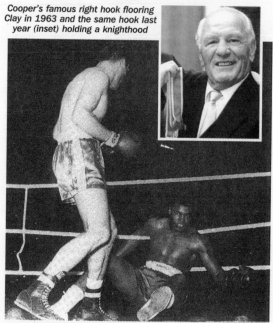

Cooper's famous right hook flooring Clay in 1963 and the same hook last year (inset) holding a knighthood

there is a chance that it may have to be cut off and sent abroad to a private collector in Japan or America," he added.

van morrison

Cooper, who was bitten on the arse by a snake two years ago, was remaining philosophical.

van tesco

"If it has to go, it has to go," he said. "But I'd love to keep it. It has a lot of sentimental value, and since I sold my Lonsdale belts I use it for holding my trousers up."

up the arse corner

Further to your request for photos of celebrities who appear to be taking it up the arse. How about this snap of Gianluca Vialli from last Saturday's Racing Post? Do I get a fiver for Ray Wilkins getting his cheesey fingers?

Ian Muir, S. Glamorgan

BURKE and HARE

BODYSNATCHING CAPERS WITH THE 19TH CENTURY LARKERS

I'LL HAVE YOUR LATE HUSBAND READY FOR BURIAL BY 3PM, MRS RICHARDS

FUNERAL PARLOUR — UNDERTAKERS

RIGHTY-OH, MR UNDERTAKER

SHORTLY — THERE. ALL NICE AND EMBALMED.

I'LL JUST LEAVE HIM ON THE WINDOWSILL TO COOL

CHORTLE! MUCH OBLIGED FOR THE CORPSE, CHUM

BAH! BURKE AND HARE

THIS'LL FIX THOSE STIFF-SNAFFLING SCAMPS

OHO!

ROTTEN EGGS

I'LL BOOBY-TRAP A CADAVER WITH SOME ROTTEN EGGS

BURKE 'N' HARE WON'T BE ABLE TO RESIST SWIPING THIS FRESH BODY

HO! HO! BUT THEY'LL SOON WIND UP WITH EGG ON THEIR FACES

WE'LL TURN THE TABLES ON THE UNDERTAKER WITH A SPOT OF EMBALMING FLUID

WOW! I'VE SLIPPED..

..AND I'VE GONE AND CROWNED THAT COPPER

CLOBBER ME WITH AN EGGY CORPSE, WOULD YOU?

FUNERAL PARLOUR — COP SHOP

HA! HA! LOOKS LIKE THE UNDERTAKER'S IN FOR A *STIFF* SENTENCE

TERRY FUCKWITT

 **THE UNINTELLIGENT CARTOON CHARACTER**

I'M SO WORRIED READERS I'VE DISCOVERED A LUMP IN MY TESTICLES

YES TERRY. WELL THE BAD NEWS IS IT'S DEFINITELY A LUMP

INFACT, THERE'S SEVERAL LUMPS IN HERE. AND SOME OF THEM ARE QUITE LARGE

HOWEVER- THE GOOD NEWS IS THIS ISN'T YOUR TESTICLES - IT'S A BOWL OF PORRIDGE

AND I'M NOT A DOCTOR I'M A CRICKET UMPIRE

TONK!

TUG!

AND YOU'RE HOLDING UP THIS TEST MATCH

COME. ALONG NOW WE'VE HAD ENOUGH OF THIS NONSENSE

EXCUSE ME- WHAT THE HELL DO YOU THINK YOU'RE DOING PLAYING CRICKET IN MY SURGERY?

GO ON! GET OUT!

SURGERY

WHAT WAS ALL THAT ABOUT THEN TERRY?

DON'T ASK ME. I'M AS THICK AS ABSOLUTE FUCK

PAULINE FOULAGE

KEN BARTLET

LYNDA BALDERSTONE

MIKE BALDERSTONE

HERE'S THE LIFT NOW.

HELLO KEN.

HELLO THERE MIKE.

LYNDA, DARLING, I'M JUST TURNING AROUND TO PUSH THE BUTTON FOR THE THIRD FLOOR.

OKAY, LOVE. SEE YOU SOON.

AT LAST WE'... STOP THIN...

I KNOW. LOOK, WE'LL H... BE BACK FROM PRESSING... IT WOULD BREAK HIS...

WHAT THE...?

MIKE..!

WHAT THE HELL IS GOING ON HERE? HOW LONG HAVE YOU BEEN MESSING AROUND WITH THAT LOSER BEHIND MY BACK?

OH, LONG ENOUGH MIKE... TWO YEARS.

TWO YEARS?!

YES MIKE. EVERY TIME YOU TURN AROUND TO PRESS THE BUTTON FOR THE 3RD FLOOR.

PART TWO

HAVE YOU SEEN THE PAPERS?

NO WHY?

IT'S NICK NYLON. THEY'VE LET HIM OUT OF PRISON.

DON'T WORRY PAULINE. THAT NO-GOOD DRUG DEALER WOULD NEVER DARE SHOW HIS FACE AROUND THIS LIFT AGAIN.

NOT AFTER TRYING TO MURDER HIS MUM, AND THEN STABBING THE LIFT ATTENDANT.

'ELLO PAULINE... LONG TIME NO SEE.

GASP!... NICK!

WHAT'S THE ... YOU LOOK L... A GHOST O...

WHAT AR... THIS WAS A ... WE DON'T...

I CAN'T ...T YOU.

THAT MAN DOESN'T HAVE A HEART. DON'T FORGET HE DESTROYED MY MARRIAGE.

...E QUICK, MIKE WILL ...UTTON ANY MINUTE. ...F HE CAUGHT US.

SO THAT'S WHAT THIS IS ABOUT! YOU'RE USING ME TO GET BACK AT HIM!

OF COURSE NOT! I LOVE YOU LYNDA.

OH KEN...MMMMMMH!

I'M TURNING BACK EARLY. SOMEONE HAD ALREADY CALLED THE LIFT TO THE 3RD FLOOR...

...IKE...!

...VCH!

GET OUT OF MY LIFE AND STAY AWAY FROM MY WIFE, BARTLET!

IT'S NOT AS SIMPLE AS THAT, MIKE.

WHAT DO YOU MEAN?

YOUR SON, MIKE, HE'S NOT YOUR SON... HE'S MINE. AND I INTEND TO TAKE HIM FROM YOU.

END OF PART ONE

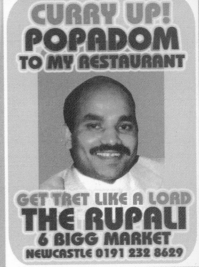

...R, GIRL? ... SEEN ...MINK.

... DOING BACK HERE NYLON? ...T LIFT BEFORE YOU GOT IN IT. ...T YOUR SORT AROUND HERE.

NO. WE DON'T WANT YOU. YOU JUST BRING TROUBLE TO THIS LIFT.

WELL PAULINE... THIS IS WHERE I GET OFF ANYWAY, BUT YOU PUT THE WORD AROUND THIS LIFT...

NICK NYLON'S BACK... AND HE'S HERE TO STAY.

PAULINE FOULAGE?

YES?

I'M AFRAID I'VE GOT SOME BAD NEWS...

YOUR DAUGHTER HAS TAKEN A DRUGS OVERDOSE.

YOU MEAN SHE'S...

YES. I'M AFRAID YOUR DAUGHTER IS...

...DEAD!

BFFM!...BFFM!...BFFM!...BFFM!... BFM-BFM-BFM!

50

GILBERT RATCHET'S
SEASIDE HOLIDAY

WE'RE OFF ON A FAMILY HOLIDAY TO THE SEASIDE, READERS

CHEZ RATCHET

CHILD'S SPEW

AND I'VE INVENTED THIS LABOUR-SAVING DEVICE FOR SPEWING DOWN THE BACK OF DAD'S NECK THROUGHOUT THE ENTIRE CAR JOURNEY

RIGHT EVERYONE — OFF WE GO!

CHILD'S SPEW

CHUNDER

FOUR HOURS LATER

HOORAY! WE'RE AT THE SEASIDE

CHUNDER

WELCOME TO SANDSEA - TWINNED WITH

LAST ONE ON THE BEACH IS A SISSY

GOSH — THE MAYOR LOOKS A BIT DEPRESSED

I'LL BUILD A SANDCASTLE FOR HIM TO JUDGE — THAT'LL CHEER HIM UP. MAYORS LOVE JUDGING SANDCASTLES

LOOK, MR MAYOR — A LOVELY SANDCASTLE

AND I'VE EVEN CONSTRUCTED THIS "MUNICIPAL·DIGNITARY·O·MATIC" TO STICK IN THE 1ST PRIZE ROSETTE FOR YOU

(SIGH) THANKS GILBERT. THIS'LL PROBABLY BE THE LAST SANDCASTLE I EVER JUDGE

IT'S THE LOCAL MAYORAL ELECTIONS THIS AFTERNOON — AND I HAVEN'T GOT A HOPE OF BEING RE-ELECTED

THANKS TO JENNIFER LOPEZ IT'S FASHIONABLE TO HAVE A GREAT BIG FULSOME ARSE NOWADAYS. JUST LOOK AT THE TUSH ON COUNCILLOR FIGGIS!

FIGGIS FOR MAYOR

VOTE FIGGIS

NO ONE WILL VOTE FOR ME WITH MY SCRAWNY BUMCHEEKS

WHAT YOUR BOTTOM NEEDS IS A BIT OF "WIGGLE"

GRUNT

EEEE EEEE

A COUPLE OF SQUIRMING PIGLETS SHOVED INTO YOUR JACKSY SHOULD DO THE TRICK

SAY! THAT'S PRETTY EFFECTIVE, GILBERT

SQUEAL

WRIGGLE

SQUIRM

GRUNT

SEE HOW MY BUTTOCKS WOBBLE AND TWITCH LIKE SOME KIND OF MAD JELLY!

WOW! ONE OF THE PIGS HAS STARTED ROOTING FOR TRUFFLES IN MY GROIN

SNORT GRUNT SNUFFLE

GET YOUR SNOUT OUT MY URETHRA YOU PORCINE PEST!

GAH!

POP!

THE STUPID PIG HAS STUCK ITS HEAD OUT ME HOG'S EYE!

WELL REALLY! WHAT DO YOU MEAN BY INDECENTLY EXPOSING YOURSELF IN THIS NON-KOSHER FASHION?

B-BUT RABBI, I CAN EXPLAIN...

I'VE NEVER BEEN SO INSULTED IN MY LIFE, ALREADY

MULTI CULTURAL "OUTRAGED VICAR" RÔLE

Dog in a Million

COMEDY double-act dog Schnorbitz has been found dead at the grave of his master, Bernie Winters.

The 10-stone St Bernard who appeared on TV with his goofy-toothed companion in the early 80s had maintained a lonely vigil by the headstone in the North London churchyard since the straightman's death in 1986.

grave

According to cemetery attendant Max Crabtree, Schnorbitz lay down by his master's grave on the day of the funeral and refused to leave for the next fifteen years. "He'd be there come rain or shine. I used to give him the leftovers from my lunchbox, or throw him the occasional bone I found when digging graves," says Crabtree.

umlaut

"I tried to take him home with me, but he'd never come. He just wanted to stay where he was. The only time he moved was when he went behind Bernie's headstone to lay his morning barker's egg."

omlette

Throughout his fifteen year watch, the faithful dog was struck by lightning (twice), and survived being attacked by crows and set on fire by vandals. It is believed he finally died after being hit by a meteorite the size of a fridge travelling at over 500 miles a second.

All clear for Nick-Nick Jim

BIG BREAK host Jim Davidson last night spoke of his relief after an agonising 3-day wait for the results of tests. Davidson discovered a lump in his throat after seeing a homeless beggar, and feared that he was developing a redeeming quality. However, tests came back clear. "I've been given the green light and I'm so relieved. I have no redeeming qualities whatsoever," said the drink-drive funnyman.

Greyfriars Schnorbitz goes to meet his master

Loveable St. Bernard Schnorbitz, 1932-2001 and (inset) his master Winters.

Faithful pets of the Stars

Schnorbitz is not alone in his lonely vigil. Showbiz graveyards are awash with celebrity pets showing loyalty above and beyond the call of duty.

TV clown Charlie Carolli will always be remembered for his inability to put up wallpaper and his love of filling people's hats with custard. But he was perhaps best known for his troupe of performing budgies.

Every day for the past 18 years, the birds he left behind have turned up at his graveside. At 13 minutes past 11 - the exact time when he died - they go through their act for their master, riding around his grave on little bicycles and going up a ladder to ring a bell.

Following his hilarious slapstick death 2 years ago,

Rod Hull was laid to rest near his home in Ipswich. He may be gone, but he is not forgotten. Guarding his grave round the clock is his double-act chum Emu.

When Michael Parkinson recently called to pay his respects, the heartbroken bird wrinkled his beak and attacked him. The veteran chat-show host was wrestled to the ground and lost a shoe in the tussle.

CONTINUED OVER...

SHAME DEFACED!

THE STANDARD of textbook defacement in British classrooms, once the highest in the world, is slipping, according to a new report by education watchdogs.

Ofsted inspectors examined Religious Education GCSE books and compared them with their counterparts from just 10 years ago. And their findings have shocked school chiefs.

basic

According to the report, more than **TWO THIRDS** of children are leaving school without even a basic understanding of how to deface R.E. textbooks properly.

fortran 77

When presented with an illustration of the Sermon on the Mount, 42% of 14-year-olds drew big round glasses on Jesus, 39% drew a Hitler moustache and coloured his teeth in, and only 19% correctly added an 8 foot snake-like penis appearing from under his robes and going into someone's ear.

pascal

One large London comprehensive was singled out for particular criticism after not a single pupil managed to satisfactorily deface a picture handed to them by inspectors.

"Year eight pupils were given forty seconds to

Teachers brought to book over pupils' lack of spunk

Mr. Clark-Five - yesterday

embellish a scene of Noah herding the animals into his ark," said report author Dave Clark-Five.

fermat

"Ten years ago, a child of thirteen would have found little difficulty in drawing a huge cock on the elephant going up Noah's robe, and adding a speech balloon reading *'Mmmm yeh. Fuk my arse'*. Not only were these pupils incapable of that, they were even unable to scribble a big hairy fanny and a pair of 'W' tits with stick nipples onto an illustration of the Virgin Mary."

custer

However, the report was not all bad news for schools. Mr. Clark-Five

THEN & NOW - How the standards have slipped

2001 | 1991

2001 | 1991

2001 | 1991

said: "One encouraging aspect of our research is that girls, who are traditionally expected to perform less well in areas such as science, technology and obscene textbook defacement, seem to be getting better results. Nowadays, if presented with an illustration of Moses descending Mount Sinai with the Ten Commandments, girls are just as likely as boys to add a speech balloon reading *'sniff my dick'*."

HOW WOULD *YOU* DO?

How much do **YOU** remember from your schooldays? Here's your chance to find out. We're offering a fancy Illustrated Victorian Bible and a box of ballpoint pens to the first reader out of the hat who correctly defaces this R.E. textbook illustration. All entries must be completed in less than 30 seconds, using a blue Biro. Send your entries to: Textbook Competition, Viz Comic, PO Box 1PT, Newcastle upon Tyne, NE99 1PT. Closing date 10th May.

Name..Age...............
Address...
....
....
Former School...
Old R.E. Teacher's Name....................................

THE CRITICS

© John Fardell '01

SUNDAY CHRONICLE ARTS SECTION

Morning, Natasha... Could you and Crispin go and spend a day with this working artist, Jane Smith? Thought it'd make an interesting article...

A little later....

Right... I think I'll set my stuff up on the pavement over here.

Ah! An outdoor installation piece... The bric-a-brac of the artist's sordid private life scattered across a public street, challenging society's hypocritical moral strait-jacket which...

No no. I'm just setting up my easel and stool.

Gasp! Now the artist has taken out a lethal looking knife!

Clearly she's about to *slice open* her body in order to create a *powerful, shocking video installation* of close-up filmed self-mutilation.

Powerful. Shocking.

No, I'm going to sharpen this pencil... I usually make a drawing in pencil before applying the watercolour paint...

Paint?! You actually use paint?

Ah, you mean you're planning a *pigment-based conceptual piece* in which you make a series of *orifice prints* to symbolise your long list of *sexual partners*...

All the People what I've shagged

No. I'm going to use the pencil and the paints to make a picture of this street... You can stay and watch if you want to but you'll have to be quiet...

Unbelievable though this sounds, it's almost as if the actual act of drawing and painting has something to do with the art-work itself.

shhh.

Scribble scrawl

Several hours later...

This is *extraordinary!* The artist has simply been sitting here... *Working!*.. Actually rendering a graphic image with *pencil and paint!*... In all my years as an art critic, I've never seen anything like it!

And what are you going to do with this piece now?

Well, basically I'll sell it...

Ah, and are you funded by the Arts Council?.. Or are you one of Charles Saatchi's new discoveries?

No neither... I'll take it in to a gallery who deal with my stuff... Someone'll probably buy it to put up in their living room.

Sell it to a member of the public?!

For them to put up in their living room?!

This isn't art at all!.. It's commercial prostitution!

Chocolate-box tat, to clutter the walls of some hideous bourgeois semi.

Come on, let's go down to that new exhibition at the South Bank... I need to cleanse my aesthetic soul with some real art...

SOUTH BANK CENTRE WAYWARD GALLERY

...and on top of my old sofa I've put a tank of formaldehyde inside which there's a DVD screen showing an endless loop of profound quotations from my own thesis on my work...

".. full of witty, ironic references.." "contains deep truths of real value to humanity."

Oh yes! This work is full of witty, ironic references...

Yet contains, at its heart, deep truths, of real value to humanity.

2001 A YOUNG BRIT ART ODYSSEY

CONTINUED OVER...

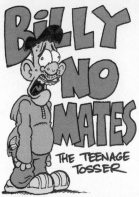

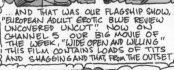

NEWS
IN CROTCHLESS
BRIEFS

with *Robert Dougall*

Not Aw-wight

Troubled comic Michael Barrymore spoke today of his battle to kick his addiction to booze clinics. The pool-death funnyman revealed how he had been visiting up ten large rehabilitation centres a day before seeking help. "It reached the stage where I was getting up in the middle of the night to dry out," he told journalistic carrion crow Martin Bashir. "I couldn't function in the morning until I'd had a couple of shots of group therapy. The Priory, AA, Betty Ford Clinic, it didn't matter as long as I got there for my treatment."

Moth out of Hell

Police called to the home of pop giant Meatloaf revealed today that they had discovered a forty stone chrysalis hanging from a bush in the conservatory. Worried neighbours called in the cops after a large number of pies accumulated on his doorstep and the star failed to show for a charity clambake. LAPD spokesman Spiro Theocropolis said: *"It appears that Mr. Loaf pupated Thursday and is now in a large silken cocoon. Our understanding at this time is that he is undergoing some sort of metamorphosis, and should emerge in a new form in the Spring."* He refused to speculate whether the singer, whose hits include *Bat Out of Hell* and *Two out of Three Ain't Bad*, would have huge gossamer wings, shimmering in a myriad of irridescent hues.

Massage in a Bottle

Radio One bosses have vowed to stand behind troubled DJ Chris Moyles after *The News of the World* published photographs of him leaving an ego massage parlour. Reporters claimed that the roly-poly unfunnyman, 38 stone, had paid a hundred pounds to have his arse licked by a posse of fawning idiots.

Russians are Coming

Russian men are enjoying up to 8 times as many orgasms as their western counterparts, according to a report published yesterday. Professor Steve Austen from Oxford University's Department of Orgasmology said: "A randy Ruskie chucks his muck 48 times each day, whereas your average Brit only manages a miserable 6 jizzbolts in a 24 hour period." Professor Austen believes it's all down to the reds' diet. *"We should take a leaf out of the Commies' book,"* he said. *"If we all ate nothing but raw beetroot, Britain would be awash with spoff."* And he angrily denied accusations that his findings had been affected by another £2m grant

for his department from the British Beetroot Board. He courted controversy last year by claiming that doubling one's intake of beetroot causes erections to become as hard as tempered steel.

Royal Blue

A home made What the Butler Saw of Queen Victoria shot by Prince Albert has surfaced on the internet. The two-minute pornographic sequence, in which the late monarch performs a sex act on her German husband before pleasuring herself with the Crown Jewels was taken on their honeymoon in 1840. The disappearance of the machine was noticed after builders had been tarmaccing the drive at Windsor Castle where the machine was kept. It is thought that it was stolen when one of them came in to use the toilet.

Full of Beans

The Provisional IRA have broken the world record for eating beans with a cocktail stick whilst wearing boxing gloves. Ten balaclava wearing paramilitaries working in relay chomped through 96 450g tins of baked beans in 10 hours, taking the record from The Ulster Volunteer Force who had helt it for fourteen years. A spokesman for the army council of the IRA was jubilant. *"We are all very pleased that we have finally taken the record. We would have liked to have had Ross and Norris McWhirter to verify it, only I'm afraid we shot one of them a few years ago,"* he quipped.

Going Ape

Boffins at San Diego University announced yesterday that have suceeded in teaching a chimpanzee to swear. Milo, a 13-year old male lowland chimp is able to communicate with his handler, calling him a wanker and telling him to stick his fucking bananas up his arse. Doctor Nam Chang in charge of the project said: "Milo is an exceptionally bright monkey, and he now has the swearing age of a 5 year old boy. We are all very excited." Dr. Chang has high hopes for the future. "We are going to carry on and by the end of 2005, we believe Milo will be able to draw a pair of tits and a big cock on the side of a bus stop," he said.

Croft ORIGINAL

She started out as a computer game, and now Lara Croft is hitting the big screen in this Summer's must-see movie. Tomb Raider, starring Angelina Jolie as the all-action heroine, is packing cinemas across Britain. But one person who certainly won't be joining the queues to see it is the real life tomb-raider who claims to be the inspiration behind the character.

Birmingham woman lays claim to Tomb Raider fame

33-year-old Walsall mother of six Tina Ringworm was raiding tombs by day and working behind the till of a 24-hour petrol station by night when she says her identity was stolen by an unscrupulous computer boss. And with the celluloid blockbuster set to net millions of pounds in royalties, Tina reckons it's time to set the record straight.

trots

In the film, Lara is an aristocratic english adventuress who trots the globe, searching for exotic jewels and treasure. From the steamy jungles of South America to the Great Wall of China, she fights off bears, dogs and tigers in her quest for gems with magical powers. But Ringworm says the film doesn't show the half of it. "The film's very good as far as it goes, but they've give it the Hollywood treatment. Tomb raiding is a dirty business, and don't let no-one tell you otherwise. For example, when Angelina Jolie fights a bear, she kills it and ends up breathing a bit heavy and perspiring slightly. The real picture isn't quite so pretty, believe me. If she'd really fought a bear, like I of loads of times, she'd be sweating like a pig and covered in blood. And she'd of shit her shorts.

squirts

"I remember this one time, I'd got right to the inner chamber of this Aztec tomb in Peru where there was some magic emeralds. I'd already had to fight a two-headed dog and a load of skellingtons. I'd just grabbed the jewels when I remembered I was on the 7 till 4 shift at the garage, and if you're a minute late he docks you an hour. I only just made it back in time. He was stood looking at his watch! But it was worth it. Them emeralds contained the secret of eternal youth and my brother sold them for £5 on his stall, and he give me £2.

runs

"On the playstation, Lara Croft gets three lives on every level. But in real life you only got one, and this was brought home to me this other time when I was raiding a tomb in the Himalayas. I was in this glass labyrinth on level four and I was trying to get away from this yeti. I couldn't shoot it because I'd used up all my bullets on a ten-foot Ninja warrior who come at me on a rope bridge. The only thing I could think of was rolling sideways every time it got close. In the end, it got tired and I done a big somersault out the labyrinth. But I knew I was already late for my shift. Luckily for me, my mate Irene covered for me and told him I was on the toilet when he come in."

wickets

But ironically, it was whilst she was working at the garage one night in 1994 that Tina believes her identity was stolen. "It was about three in the morning and this thin bloke come in with glasses. I remember he had a white Astra van and he was getting £8 of DERV and a pepperami. He seemed in no hurry and we got chatting. I told him how I'd just gone up to £1.75 an hour and then the subject got round to tomb raiding. I told him all about my adventures, and he seemed quite interested.

tickets

"He went on his way and I thought no more about it. Then, the next night I was on 10 till 8 and about midnight I seen this man on the news and it was him. He was Bill Gates and he'd just invented playstation. There was Lara Croft on it and I immediately realised it was me."

rickets

With the Tomb Raider film set to break all box office records, Tina reckons it's high time her unwitting contribution was recognised.

derbyshire neck

"Bill Gates has made a lot of money out of me and it's only right that I get a fair share of what he's got. I want £200 or I told him I'm going to write a letter to the Have Your Say page in the Walsall Express and Star."
A spokesman for Microsoft in Seattle denied Tina's claims. "Bill Gates no longer owns a white Astra van," he told us.

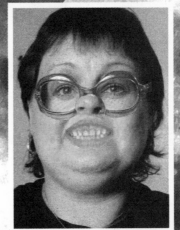 

SPOT THE DIFFERENCE - Tina Ringworm (left) could spell double trouble for billion-squillionaire Gates. Pretend Croft, Angelina Jolie (right) .

Letterbocks

Star Letter

Letterbocks
Viz Comic
P.O. Box 1PT
Newcastle-upon-Tyne
NE99 1PT

E-mail letters@letterbocks.com

● Who says we're not getting a good deal from our train services since privatisation? Admittedly the fares have increased out of all proportion and the journeys are often hours longer that they were ten years go, but the fine for pulling the emergency chain is £50, exactly the same as it was in 1962. That's what I call value for money.

Foz
Tottenham

● In a recent issue, you asked for pictures of people who looked like they were being taken up the arse. I'd like to

submit this picture of ex-Foreign Secretary Robin Cook getting his shit shoved back a fortnight.

Paul Dixon
Stakeford

● The other day I bought £50 worth of dope from a man behind a pub, butwhen I got it home it turned out to be an Oxo cube. I reported the matter to the police straight away, but did they want to know? Did they hell. They were probably too busy prosecuting motorists for driving 20mph over the speed limit or pulling someone over to check the tread on his tyres.

M. Hall
Tipton

Court out

● Whilst listening to Radio 5 Live a few weeks ago, I heard the reporter say that the Wimbledon Tennis Championships were just around the corner. Imagine my disappointment when I walked to the end of my street, only to find a dog being sick under an abandoned Ford Escort.

Stitch Mitchell
East Bradford

● Peter Sutcliffe could be released from Broadmoor Mental Institution if he were made to wear a little bell round his neck. This has certainly worked on my cat which used to kill no end of birds, but has not killed one since I fixed it to his collar.

A. Carabino
Fulham

Scaramouche, Scaramouche, did he kill the Jill Dando?

● On the face of it, it seems that Barry Bulsara had been convicted of Jill Dando's murder on the flimsiest of circumstantial evidence. After his conviction, however, certain facts came to light that paint a picture of a man quite capable of committing such an act. The sad fact is, that we may never know the truth of his guilt or innocence, because only one man knows for certain whether or not Bulsara is Jill's murderer, and that is Bulsara himself. Well, him and the bloke who actually did it, obviously.

Christina Ratcliffe
Hull

● Here's a good heading that the sub-editor slipped past his boss.

Adam Hewitt
Reading

* £20 is on it's way to the staff of the Surrey Mirror.

● With reference to the letter from the man who pissed in Jamie Oliver's window box (issue 108), that's nothing. Five years ago I worked as a baggage handler at Manchester airport. One day I saw Ulrika Jonnson checking her suitcase in for the Heathrow Shuttle, so I made my way down to the baggage hall and awaited the 'prize bag'. As colleagues kept watch, the bag was thrown to me inside the aircraft container and I put Ulrika's knickers on my head forthwith. As I opened her washbag and took the top off her Ladyshave, I was awestruck to see a solitary golden pube adorning the razor foil. At this point I was rushed by my excited colleagues just as

I was about to put the beauty in my mouth for safe keeping.
I also once bent Gladiator Wolf's golf clubs through 45° and poured a tin of aircraft engine oil on Stan Boardman's suit. Blame that on the fucking Germans, you gap-toothed cunt.

A. Fairuz
e-mail

● So pop Queen Madonna objects to people calling her *Madge*. Frankly, after charging the best part of £100 for a ticket to her Earl's Court concert, £25 for a programe and £60 for a poxy T-shirt, I reckon she's getting off quite lightly with Madge. *Greedy Fucking Yankee Whore* would be more appropriate.

Brian Naomi
London

VET
HE WON'T STOP SCRATCHING

● Recent reports show that far from costing the country money, Her Majesty the Queen actually *brings in* £10 million a year. Instead of trying to abolish the Monarchy,

why doesn't the government turn all the unemployed into monarchs, thus creating a net income for the country of £10,000 billion pounds annually. That's a tax free windfall of £170,000 for every man, woman and child in the country.

D. Milligan
Jesmond

● Raymond Blanc says that preparing food is an act of love. Well seeing as he runs a resaurant and does it for money, that makes him a prostitute.

G. Whittaker
London

● Further to G. Whittaker's letter (above). I'm a chef in a well known high street fast food restaurant and cooking is indeed an act of love for me. That's because I wank in the burgers.

R.M.
Newcastle

Nut funny

● I never took the subject of testicular cancer seriously, only ever referring to it to make cheap jokes. Only when the Cancer Research Campaign highlighted awareness with a moving picture of Denise Van Outen putting her hand down Julian Clary's trousers whilst pulling a Kenneth Williams *'Ooh, Matron!'* face was the full enormity of this terrible disease brought home to me.

You must be nuts, Denise

Paul Halliwell
London

● Barry Bulsara may have had a particle of firearm discharge in his pocket, but this does not prove that he fired the gun that killed Jill Dando. It seemed that there was a strong chance that the coat may have suffered forensic contamination. Seven witnesses further weakened the case against him by describing him in turn as having long, short,

straight, curly, thick and receding hair, wearing a blue suit, a black suit or waxed jacket. However, I feel that his defence team missed one vital piece of evidence that would certainly have proved his innocence - he's not a fucking lorry driver.

S. Jones
Runcorn

● Jesus Christ! He's at it again.

Paul Dixon
Stakeford

Film bluff

● The other day whilst listening to Radio 5 Live, the presenter informed anyone who enjoyed action-packed movies, that the film *Tomb Raider*, starring Angelina Jolie would be right up their street. Imagine my disappointment when I found the same dog being sick under the same abandoned Ford Escort.

Stitch Mitchell
East Bradford

Bum Notes
-Britain's LIVELIEST tramp correspondence column

Each issue, Bum Notes asks for *YOUR* opinions on a different aspect of tramps. Here's what you had to say about this week's Tramp Topic... Begging

...in my opinion, simply buying the Big Issue only goes part of the way in solving the problem of homeless people begging. What I do is roll up my copy and strike them smartly across the nose, saying 'NO' in a firm, clear voice. Like my dog, they'll soon learn not to beg again.
Jane Rowlands, market researcher

...begging for spare change in the street must be very humiliating. For this reason, before I hand over my 10p, I make the tramp do a little dance for me and my friends. That way, he has provided a service and has earned the money, thereby gaining some self respect.
John Wilson, librarian

...if a tramp asks you for some money for a cup of tea, chances are they'll go and spend it on cigarettes and beer. Mind you, I've got an off-licence, so I say give it to them.

Frank Welsh, shopkeeper

...begging is antisocial behaviour and will not stop until the public take a firm stand against beggars. When asked for change, I let these people know in no uncertain terms that they will get nothing from me by quickening my pace, looking at my shoes and mumbling 'sorry, no'.
Aiden Clifford, graphic designer

...most of these beggars are just con men. I was once about to hand over 10p to one unfortunate looking fellow when suddenly a mobile phone rang in his pocket. I couldn't believe it! It was the garage telling him that his car was ready. A Rolls Royce, if you please. And a solid gold one at that. With mink seats!

Charles Lewethwaite, retired brigadier

TOP TIPS

BY GRABBING hold of a charity letter and twisting it sideways, it is possible to remove the free pen without opening it and subjecting yourself to all that guilt.
Phil Hunt
Stroud

WHINGEING southern puffs. Avoid your annual moaning about water shortages and hosepipe bans by filling all your buckets when you get flooded in the winter.
Peckham
e-mail

POTHOLERS. Take a tip from cats and avoid getting stuck in holes by growing a moustache to the exact width of your body.
Ryan Lloyd
Rhyl

BOY racers. Give your car that lowered suspension, ground-hugging racing look by driving around with 12 paving slabs in the boot and a bag of builders' sand under each front seat.
James Augustini
Leicester

A MIXTURE of sour cream and mashed-up blackberries makes excellent imitation bird shit to apply to your neighbour's car after he's washed it.
Woody
Walsall

AMATEUR astronomers. Avoid total blindness by viewing the sun through a telescope rather than binoculars.
Simon Hollingworth
Norwich

BIRDWATCHERS. Save hours sitting around waiting to see which species land on your birdtable. Simply mix the food with rat poison and

hey presto - dozens of birds laying around the foot of the table for you to inspect and tick off in your book at leisure.
Stot & Naylor
Scunthorpe

WAIT till your neighbours get into their car, then fool them into thinking the handbrake doesn't work by pulling their house backwards.
Jimmy Docherty
e-mail

SWAP your wife's factor 35 sunblock for Brylcreem on the first day of your foreign holiday. Then when she's confined to the hotel bed with sun-

stroke, nip out and shag loads of birds from Manchester.
P. Jacobs
Walthamstow

DOG owners. Stop your pet drooling whenever you fry bacon by placing an odour-eater under each rasher as it cooks.
L. Marrion
Gloucester

ALCOHOLICS. The foil bag from inside a wine box makes an excellent pillow to go to sleep on and provides a handy source for your 'Hair of the Dog' on waking.
Ben Cormack
Castle Douglass

GILBERT RATCHET

Nit's a MIRACLE!

Mercy plea as baby Fleanix survives against all odds

Pressure is mounting on the Prime Minister to spare a baby headlouse found alive after twenty minutes under a pile of carcasses on a schoolboy's head.

The tiny survivor, named Fleanix, was missed by insecticidal shampoo as she lay huddled beside her dead mother.

By our Big Chief Home Affairs Correspondent

Stanley um Two-Rivers

parasite

Now the nit nurse who found the week-old orphan parasite is begging education officials to spare her from being popped on the side of a sink.

Nora - Heartbroken

School nurse, Nora Lakeman had been treating children after an outbreak of lice was discovered in a classroom at Talbot Road Infant School in Blackpool.

parachute

Nora, 42, said "I found the little nit when I was running a comb through the head of one of the boys in 2B."

"It broke my heart when I saw little Fleanix. She was lying next to her mum, trembling and looking bewildered. How she survived the shampoo I'll never know. It's a miracle."

paraquat

Big hearted Nora took the nit home immediately and has been hand feeding her on dandruff with a pair of tweezers. "It was touch and go for a while, but now she's doing really well, considering what she has been through," said Nora. "It would be evil to kill her at this point."

parasol

There was an outcry after officials from the LEA insisted that all nits must be destroyed to prevent the outbreak spreading to neighbouring schools.

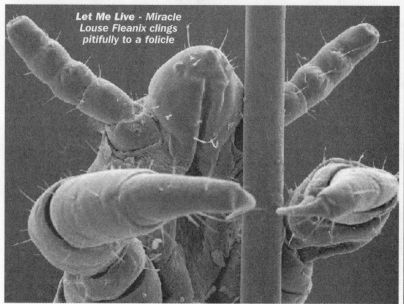

Let Me Live - Miracle Louse Fleanix clings pitifully to a folicle

Hope amongst the carnage - little Fleanix huddles beside her mother's corpse (right)

"She was lying next to her mum, trembling. How she survived the shampoo I'll never know"

IT'S TIME TO STOP THE KILLING!

"For Fax Sake, Save Fleanix", say Big-Hearted Viz Readers

THOUSANDS of mentally subnormal readers bombarded Viz yesterday with badly spelled and punctuated faxes, e-mails and petitions begging Education chiefs to spare Fleanix the Miracle louse's tiny life.

Elderly residents at a day centre signed a petition saying: "Please save that innocent little nit. If you can't find a home for her, she can come and live in our hair"

plight

Even hardened criminals have been moved to tears by Fleanix's plight. Broadmoor lifer Arnold Nonce begged "Please, God, spare baby Fleanix. She is a symbol of hope for us all."

Mrs Bollocks from Cheltenham said "Surely there has been enough slaughter. this innocent dickie has already been through so much in her short life."

One of the thousands of faxes we've received - this one from 46-year-old Dr. Derek Taylor of Hull

What do YOU think?

Should Fleanix be burst to prevent the spread of nits? Or should a special case be made in this instance?
E-mail us with your credit card number and let us know what YOU think. And don't forget to include the expiry date.

IS *THIS* ANY WAY TO TREAT OUR DEAD?

SHOCKING EXPOSÉ
by our 'Is This Any Way to Treat Our Dead' correspondent Diddy David Hamilton's wife.

The Mirror
Monday January 15 2001
WIN £1M GUARANTEED

SICKENING

Seven bodies dumped in wooden boxes then thrown into holes in the ground...

The head of a Bedford undertaking firm resigned yesterday after it was revealed that bodies were routinely *LEFT LYING* on his premises in wooden boxes before *BEING LOWERED* into holes in the ground.

On other occasions, it is alleged that bodies have simply been SET ON FIRE to get rid of them.

dug

Leonard Duxbury, head of funeral directors Shadrack & Duxbury, quit after *Daily Mirror* photographers dug up several coffins and prised the lids off.

churn

Mechanical engineer David Nipsy, whose late grandfather, Arthur was one of the corpses concerned, was shocked.

"I can't describe what I felt when I saw my decomposing grandad on the front of the paper," he told us.

EXCLUSIVE!

Duxbury (above) - yesterday and (right), Mirror editor Piers Morgan prises open a coffin to reveal Arthur Nipsy's decaying foot

"It was shock, outrage and sadness, tinged with a glimmer of hope that I might get some compensation. My grandad fought in the War, so to treat him like this is disgraceful. It just seems so undignified to bury him in the ground like a big potato."

shake

Adele Barse flew from New Zealand six months after her mother's death, to finalise the sale of her house and property.

"When I arrived at the undertakers they just handed me a jar of

David Nipsy - too shocked to comment, yesterday

ashes," said a tearful Barse. "She had been burnt so I couldn't even recognise her."

marketing board

Adele's father died five years ago, and his funeral was handled by Shadrack & Duxbury. She now fears they may have simply buried him in a hole. "My father worked for the gas board for forty years," she told us. "He always wore shiny shoes and he never even had so much as a parking ticket. It is unbelievably callous to simply leave him in the ground to be eaten by worms and moles."

Lord, *Help Us!*
with *Abdul Latif, Lord of Harpole*

Dear Lord of Harpole Please help me, as I am at my wits end. My husband is up for a pay rise and in order to impress his boss, he has invited him and his wife for dinner. His boss is a great fan of curries, and foolishly my husband told him what a great curry cook I was. The truth is, I have never cooked a curry in my life, and I don't know my madras from my elbow.

I just know the evening is going to be a disaster. My husband will lose his job, our house will be repossessed and I will have to go back on the game. They will be here in two hours. Lord, help me.

June Medford, Surbiton

Lord Harpole says... Firstly, do not be cross with your husband. Inviting the boss for dinner is a good way to "curry" his favour. Secondly, have no fears about cooking the meal. I, Mr. Abdul Latif, Lord of Harpole, am only a premium rate phonecall away. You, and in fact any Viz reader, can have the benefit of my years of experience as Newcastle's leading curry expert by dialling CurryTalkLive on 0906 515 1047. I will be able to personally give you advice about any curry-related topics. Calls cost just £1.50 per minute, so remember to get permission from the bill payer. All callers must be over 18, which since you are married, I assume you are. I'm sure with my help, your husband will get that pay rise which should help pay for the phonecall.

Dear Lord of Harpole I've done a stupid thing. For years my wife and I have been saving up to go to Australia to see our grandchildren. By scrimping and saving, we had got nearly £10,000 in the building society. Then yesterday, like a fool I went into Ladbroke's and bet the lot that giraffes don't make any noise. They gave me odds of 5-7. Now my brother, who is a giraffe handler at the zoo, has told me that they sometimes bleat like a lamb. I'm scared I've lost all our money. Please put me out of my misery by telling me if giraffes make a noise or not. Lord, help me.

Tony Gubba, Chessington

Lord Harpole says... I, Abdul Latif, Lord of Harpole, have good news and bad news. The bad news is that giraffes do occasionally bleat like lambs. So you've lost your bet, you won't ever see your grandchildren, and your wife is probably going to kill you. But the good news is you can make it up to her by cooking a wonderful curry and I'll tell you how on CurryTalkLive on 0906 515 1047.

Do YOU have a curry query? Perhaps you're puzzled over poppadoms, or you're in a tizzy over a tikka. What ever your curry conundrums, call The Lord of Harpole on CurryTalkLive on 0906 515 1047. Calls cost £1.50 /min. And at that price, it's probably best to get the bill payer's permission first, or call from work. Over 18s only.

Aldridge PRIOR
HE'S A HOPELESS LIAR

ALDRIDGE IS VISITING AMERICA...

UNITED STATES PASSPORT CONTROL

ALDRIDGE PRIOR?

NO. ACTUALLY I'M SADDAM HUSSEIN'S COUSIN. ALDRIDGE HUSSEIN. I USED TO BE IN THE S.A.S.

YOU'RE NOT ALDRIDGE PRIOR?

YES.

NO.

ACTUALLY YES. I HOLD THE WORLD RECORD FOR EATING OYSTERS. STATES PASSPORT CONTROL

WHAT IS THE PURPOSE OF YOUR VISIT?

I'VE GOT A MILLION POUND WORTH OF GRADE A CRACK HEROIN UP MY BOTTOM.

MY MATE ALLY ROSS OFF THE NEWS OF THE WORLD FOUND IT IN LIAM GALLAGHER'S DUSTBIN.

SO...

I CAYN'T SEE DIDDLEY-SQUAT UP THERE, BUDDY.

ARIFLEX ARSE CAMERA

SHOVE!

IT'LL BE FURTHER UP. YOU'RE JUST LOOKING INSIDE THE FALSE BOTTOM THEY SEWED INSIDE MY REAL ONE. IT COST A MILLION POUND TO DO IT.

YOU SEEM TO HAVE WASTED OUR TIME, MR. PRIOR. WE CAYN'T FIND ANY DRUGS ANYWHERE UP YOUR ASS.

ARIFLEX ARSE CAMERA

THE CAMERA'S COME OUT YOUR MOUTH NOW.

SO...

WHAT IS THE PURPOSE OF YOUR VISIT?

ERM... YOU SEE THIS FOUNTAIN PEN? IT'S REALLY A GUN.

SIR. ARE YOU THREATENING ME WITH A FIREARM?

WHIP!

I'M NOT REALLY ALDRIDGE PRIOR. I'M CARLOS THE JACKAL. ACTUALLY I'VE COME HERE TO ASSASSINATE GEORGE W. BUSH. YEAH, MY MATE COLONEL GADAFFI HAS GIVEN ME A MILLION POUND TO DO IT.

AND I SHOT PHIL MITCHELL.

SO...

I'M NOT SCARED. MY MATES ARE GOING TO RESCUE ME IN A HELICOPTER.

ALIVE

DEAD

ANYWAY, I'VE GOT A MECHANICAL HEART, AND ELECTRICITY JUST MAKES ME STRONGER.

BZZZZ

POP!

THOK!

ZZZZZZ

WOOWOOWOOWOOWOOH WOOWOOWOOWOOWOON

THE MODERN PARENTS

John Fardell

December 24....

Wow! It's snowed in the night!.. Brilliant!

Oh Tarquin!..

There's nothing brilliant about snow if you're a **homeless refugee** or an **endangered hedgehog**, struggling to survive the winter.

All this **strange weather** is very **worrying**... Man's global pollution is affecting the climate.

But it's **supposed** to snow in the middle of winter!

Ah, that's what the multinational capitalists' Christmas card propoganda is designed to make you believe!.. They're trying to cover up global warming.

How can **snow** be caused by global warming?

Tarquin, the Earth's eco-system is more **complex** than Western science can explain... It's all to do with the imbalance of Yin Yang energy...

This is **boring!** Come on, Guin. Let's get out to the park...

Later...

Whoops! Sorry!

Oh **Tarquin!** Toboggan racing endorses the concept of competitive sport and encourages a reliance on private, single-occupant, high-speed, anti-pedestrian forms of transport.

Can't you find a more **constructive** activity?

Well, we've made a snowman.

I hope you've made a snow-**woman** as well...

...You must practice an equal opportunities policy for snowpersons.

Oh yes, we've made a snow-woman too... Come and see...

HEE HEE HEE   HEE HEE HEE

Tarquin, I don't know **who** these figures are supposed to represent but this one's clearly an offensive caricature of **all** womanhood...

We don't believe in censorship but I don't think it would be **responsible** to leave this one standing either, where it could cause offence to..to the **beard-wearing community** in general...

Aw! We took ages to make them! WHAAH!

This snow must be polluted with toxins from nuclear testing. It's bringing out some very anti-social behaviour in you two...

Tarquin, I can't **believe** you've been teaching Guinevere to throw **lethal projectiles** at people!

It was only a snowball!

Yes, well, if you train him to throw snowballs now, he'll be bombarding civilians with **napalm bombs** when he's older... That's how the military-industrial complex indoctrinates young people.

What are you doing in the park, anyway? I thought you didn't like the snow.

We're gathering firewood for our camp...

See?...This is our Climate-Change-Research Igloo Encampment... We're going to live at one with nature, like the Innuit...

I'm going to make a Lentil Bake Surprise over the camp fire...

I thought Innuits ate *seals* and *walruses*.

Well, if they do, it's only because the White Man has deprived them of access to basic vegan recipies.

We've got enough supplies for the four of us to stay here for two weeks.

Wholemeal Free Range LENTILS

GARLIC

Stay here !?.. For *two weeks*!?... You must be *mad*! It's Christmas Day tomorrow!.. We're going over to Uncle Eddie's.

No we're not!

We're going to stay here and keep vigil... It's up to expert ecologists like us to monitor the effects of climate change...

Look, all these trees have lost their leaves... That's a well known symptom of acid rain.

This must be acid snow...

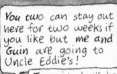

You two can stay out here for two weeks if you like but me and Guin are going to Uncle Eddie's!

Tarquin, don't be silly... You and Guinevere owe it to future generations to stay here in our Innuit settlement.

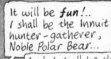

It will be *fun*!.. I shall be the Innuit hunter-gatherer, Noble Polar Bear...

And I shall be the Innuit wise-woman, Serene Orca... What are you two going to be?

We're going to be warm and comfortable, in a proper house with proper central heating, having a proper Christmas with proper food and proper presents, *that's* what *we're* going to be... Bye!

Come back here!

Quick !.. Into the car... I mean, the Research Camp Support Vehicle... We'll catch them up and *make* them stay !

I'll take a short cut across the frozen lake.

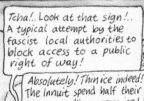

Tcha!.. Look at that sign!.. A typical attempt by the fascist local authorities to block access to a public right of way!

Absolutely! Thin ice indeed! The Innuit spend half their lives travelling across ice!

DANGER THIN ICE

You have to *trust* nature... Water and ice are *female*, *supportive* elements... We did it on my *Embracing Your Inner Nature Goddess* workshop.

Later...

Well, I hope your parents are alright, camping out in this weather... Mind you, they're real experts on all that outdoor environmental stuff, aren't they?

The g..g..global warming m..must have g..got *really* b..bad for the ice to b..be *that* thin!

The c..c..council should be forced to p..p..put up warning signs... It's all a big cover up!

© John Fardell 2001

77

Catch a Thievin

We see them on stage and screen, we welcome them into our homes without a second thought. We even entrust our children into their care for hours each day. But is our faith in the stars misplaced?

With celebrities regularly convicted of crimes ranging from drink-driving to murder, can we really trust them as far as we could throw them?

In an experiment that provided an instantaneous snapshot of the honesty of top personalities, we left eight brand new bicycles at a variety of showbiz locations. All were left unlocked, whilst our hidden cam-

Shocking Investigation
By *GREG GLEET* & *CHARLIE KNOBCHEESE*

eras watched and waited to catch the stars red-handed. Sadly, we didn't have to wait long.

In Hollywood, it took just *9 minutes* for an international movie star to swipe our bike. 6000 miles away in Newcastle, a household name pedalled it away after less than *30 seconds*.

The shocking pictures in this shocking investigation will shock you. It seems that when opportunity knocks, the stars are only too willing to take us all for a ride.

g.gleet&c.knobcheese@viz.co.uk

Sham
who sto
in bro

Take That and Scarper...

1 IT'S a case of daylight *Robbie-ery* when we leave our £100 top of the range mountain bike leaning against the gate of a trendy Soho winebar.

After just half-an-hour, pop bad boy **Robbie Williams** strolls past giving our bike a casual glance before moving on. Five minutes later he's back.

Williams, who ripped off his skin in his video hit *Rock DJ* was only too happy to *rip off* our bike, and wasted no time getting into the saddle and riding off towards his penthouse flat in Chelsea.

SOHO..................35mins

Stroke of Luck...

LONDON......2hrs

Unlocked bike makes his day...

2 IT'S 10.15 in the morning when we leave our bike leaning against railings just around the corner from Universal Studios.

After just 7 minutes, the familiar figure of **Clint Eastwood** ambles over to take a closer look. 2 minutes later and he's back, feeling lucky.

A mere *fistful of dollars* would have bought multi-millionaire Clint a similar bike, but with a quick look round to make sure the coast's clear, *Dirty Harry* makes a *clean* getaway.

HOLLYWOOD........9mins

Fatman and Robbin'...

VIENNA..............5

...g Star

...of celebs
...e our bikes
...d daylight

Goodbye Yellow Bike Rode...

5 OUR smart touring cycle has been propped up by a tennis club in the South of France since early on Saturday morning.

The glittering clientelle of exclusive Nice tennis club have given it barely a second look all day. But rock star **Elton John** has other ideas. It seems that Elton believes Saturday night's alright... *for stealing bikes!*

He doesn't realise we've caught it all on film, and there'll be *'Elt toupee'*, after our bike vanishes into thin *hair*.

NICE.........12hrs 42mins

3 IT'S four in the afternoon when we casually leave our 10-speed Carrera racer nestling against a wall by London's Regent's Park.

Passers by ignore it for more than 2 hours, until her Royal Highness **Princess Margaret** stops to give it a right royal once-over. But the Queen's sister isn't in any hurry.

She hangs back to check that the owner isn't nearby before swiftly swinging her leg over the crossbar and *hotfooting* it away in the direction of Kensington Palace. .

...ins

Jen behaving Brad-ly...

NEW YORK.........16mins

6 OUR bike has only been standing on the corner of Broadway for a quarter of an hour.

Many stars have already walked past and given it the once-over, including Sylvester Stallone, Woody Allen and the Chuckle brothers. But it's **Brad Pitt** who finally makes a move on it.

Friends star wife **Jennifer Aniston** out keeps toot while the *Fight Club* star brazenly hops on board. He can't believe his luck as he pedals off, giving Aniston a croggy towards Times Square.

4 WHEN we lean our bike against the bins behind the Vienna Opera House, it takes less than an hour for us to discover that thieves operate in this *aria*.

Salad-dodging tenor **Luciano Pavarotti** sidles up after a mere 52 minutes and wastes no time snaffling our bike.

With a shady glance over his shoulder, he slyly tries the bike for size before sliding his enormous arse into the saddle and wobbling unsteadily away into the Austrian capital's maze of back streets.

...ins

Unchained Melody...

7 TO the North East of England, where we leave our bike propped up underneath the Tyne Bridge.

After a mere 28 seconds, *Soldier Soldier* star **Robson Green** skulks into view and gives it the once over. Pint-sized Robson certainly doesn't look *green* when it comes to bike theft, and after a quick glance both ways he's in like *Flynn*.

Halfway across the bridge, he stops to lower the saddle, then he's off pedalling as fast as his little legs will carry him to his million pound Gateshead mansion.

NEWCASTLE........28secs

Next week: *We test the fat stars' honesty by leaving some pies to cool on windowledges.*

1. Peebles shepherd Andrew Selkirk was going out, leaving Black Bag, his faithful border binliner in charge of a litter of 15 little crisp bags. "Och, laddie. I'm awa' tae the tattoo parlour in Cappercleuch. Tak guid care o'ma wee crispy baggies. Dinnae let nae hairm come tae 'em." Selkirk knew he could rely on his polythene pal to keep a watchful eye on his charges.

2. The shepherd had only been gone a few minutes when a tall, thin woman approached the garden. It was Mrs McDe Ville, the teacher at the local junior school. "Jings! Whit lovely little crisp baggies," she cooed. "I must tak 'em back tae ma school." In a trice, she had scooped up the litter from under the hedge and stuffed them in her pockets.

3. Black Bag knew Andrew would be heartbroken to find the crisp bags gone when he returned. In desperation he fluttered round the teacher's ankles to trip her up, but Mrs McDe Ville was having none of it. "Git awa' frae me, ye pesky bag. I'm no in the mood fer any o' ye games. These wee crisp baggies are mine," she cried, as she made her way to the school.

4. Peering through an open window into the stockroom, Bag saw Miss McDe Ville talking to a couple of burly classroom assistants. "Listen here. Including this last 15, we've got 101 crisp bags. That's muckle enough 'Books fer Schools' coupons fer a copy o' 'Stig o' the Dump'. So get cuttin' those bags up, the noo!" So that was her game. Bag had to act fast to save the terrified little packets.

5. The lazy assistants were in no hurry to start. "Come alang, Hamish. We'll hae oorselves a bonny braw cuppy o' tea and a hobnob afore we start choppin' up them baggies." Black Bag saw his chance and with the help of a sudden gust of wind, slipped in through the stockroom window. A tin of blackboard paint teetering on a shelf gave the crafty bin liner an idea.

6. SPLASH! Bag knocked the paint all over the crisp packets. Soon, they were all as black as he was. "Whit's them, Hamish?" asked one of the assistants, as the 101 bags fluttered to freedom right under their noses. "Och, it's nothin'. Just a muckle load o' wee bin-liners. Dinnae fret yersel." Within minutes, Black Bag had led all the packets out of the school.

7. "Why have ye nae started cuttin' up those crisp bags yet, ye lazy pair o' neep heeds?" demanded Mrs McDe Ville furiously. "Noo I'll hae tae dae it ma sel." But when she entered the stockroom, the angry teacher couldn't believe her eyes. "Crivvens!" she screeched. "Ye've let a' ma baggies escape! A'll tak ma hand off yer faces, ye deep-fried twatties!"

8. The wily binliner knew the lanes around Peebles like the back of his hand, and it wasn't long before he and his 101 disguised friends had made their way back to the safety of the lawn in front of Andrew Selkirk's but'n'ben. And what a sight met the shepherd's eyes when he walked through the gate. "Help m'boab!" he laughed. "A 101 wee'uns. Bag, ye sly auld de'il!"

ROGER MELLIE
THE MAN ON THE TELLY

SO WHAT DO YOU RECKON TOM, EH? THE A-Z OF CHARLES AND CAMILLA...

... 26 SHOWS, ONE A WEEK!

A FOR ANAL — AND DO THEY DO IT...

B FOR BREASTS...WE'VE GOT HER EX-WINDOW CLEANER TO TELL US WHAT THEY'RE LIKE, AND WE'VE DUG AN OLD BRA OUT OF THE BIN AT HIGHGROVE..

C IS FOR COCK... THAT'S A SCREAM THAT EPISODE, TOM

HONESTLY, HE'S HUNG LIKE A FUCKING CHINESE MOUSE

THE WHOLE SERIES IS IN THE CAN, TOM. WE'RE ONLY MISSING 'W'...

YOU WOULDN'T STICK THIS MASK ON AND DROP YOUR TROUSERS, WOULD YOU?

WE'LL USE SOFT FOCUS. NO ONE WILL GUESS..

NO I WILL NOT, ROGER

I CAN'T BELIEVE YOU'VE MADE THIS SERIES. NO ONE'S GOING TO BUY IT

IT'S TASTELESS, IT'S TACKY. IT'S A COMPLETE INVASION OF THEIR PRIVACY

CHRIST ALMIGHTY, YOU'VE HAD SOME STUPID IDEAS IN YOUR TIME, ROGER, BUT THIS ONE LEAVES THEM STANDING

HOLD ON, HOLD ON. IT WASN'T MY IDEA

EH!?! THEN WHO...

TWO SUGARS ISN'T IT, MR MELLIE?

THAT'S RIGHT, ED — AND FETCH A PACKET OF HOBNOBS, WILL YOU?

the SID the SEXIST

ITS THE FIRST DAY OF THE LADS' TWO WEEK BREAK...

I THINK YUZ'LL AGREE LADS, THAT THE BEAUTY OF Y' SPANISH HOLIDUR IS THAT NEE-ONE'S KEEPIN' AN EYE ON Y' PINT COONT F' WHEN Y' ALLOWED A PISS

AYE BAZ-IT'S AALMURST LIKE YE CAN HAVE A PISS WHENEVER Y FEEL LIKE IT

AYE

AYE. FUCKIN' SMASHIN'

HAD ON SID-HOW MANY TIMES DID YE SHAKE YER AWLD MAN AFTA YER PISS JUST THEN?

EH?! ERM- I DIVVINT KNA. ABOOT FAWA?

FAWA!? FAWA?! FUCKIN' HELL SID

EH?!

SID MAN! DO YER NOT NAA NOWT? ANY MORE THAN THREE SHAKES IS A WANK!

AYE SID- WANKIN' IN A PUBLIC BOG!

IN FRONT O' YER MATES AN AAL

AYE. Y' FILTHY HOM

BUT LADS- NEE ONE TELT US ABOOT THAT RULE, MAN.

IT'S NEE GOOD SID. YEE'VE DONE IT NOW.

TWO WEEKS LATER...

HOWAY LADS - ITS LIKE I KEEP SAYIN', STRITE UP ON ME MAMS LIFE- I WUZ AANLY TRYING TO SHAKE THE DRIPS OFF THE END!

CAN YU HEAR A FUCKIN' PORVORT ANYONE?!

Letterbocks

Letterbocks
Viz comic
PO Box 1PT
Newcastle upon Tyne
NE99 1PT

AFFIX STAMP HERE

Star Letter

Manufacturers of Dulux 'Once'. I think the word you are looking for is 'twice'.

**K.C. Jones,
Steaminanarollin**

With the Queen Mum just celebrating her 101st birthday, wouldn't it have been glorious for the country if someone had painted a number 1 on her left arse cheek and a number 1 on her right. She could then have bent over, spreading her glorious, yet mature arse cheeks to display 101, broadcast live to the nation. That would have been a birthday to remember.

**Sir Fingerbobs
Turkey**

Pig's Trotter

How did Jack Frost ever become a copper? He's too short-arsed by half.

**A. Jackson
Grimsby**

"You treat your dad like he was a taxi driver!" my mum complained the other day. And I had to admit she was right. I'd just shot him in the back of the head.

**Leslie Grantham
Walford**

I saw the inside of a wheelchair-bound driver's car the other day and was astounded by the modifications that had been made to allow them to drive safely on the road. What if the same amount of time and trouble had been spent designing a vehicle specially made for a drunk driver? I'm sure the market for this sort of car would be huge. So come on, car manufacturers, get your thinking caps on and make our roads safer.

**Edd Hillman
e-mail**

A while ago I had a wheel nicked off my car. Barry George lived not 400 miles away. Coincidence?

**T. Rusling
Cottingham**

I am proud to announce that my cock has been chosen as the official snack of the women's synchronised swimming team for the 2004 Olympics.

**Dave Brookes
e-mail**

Why are the police spending so much time and money collecting names for the national paedophile register? Surely they could just ask for a copy of the membership lists of all British caravaning clubs.

**AMN
e-mail**

For peat's sake

Please can someone help me? I can't seem to think of another purpose for multi-purpose compost, other than for growing plants in.

**Leo Stitch
e-mail**

For fox sake

As an urban fox, I am constantly disgusted by the level of hard core pornography we see on the BBC, often in the early evening. The other night, as I watched TV through Rumbellows window with my litter of seven cubs I was shocked to see a nature documentary showing two foxes having doggy style sex

**A. Fox
The Den**

I'm sick and tired of reading in problem pages about premature ejaculation being a problem for men. Surely premature ejaculation is a woman's problem.

**Lee Nelson
e-mail**

Summit to think about

If heat rises, how come the top of Mount Everest is so fucking cold?

**Sir E. Hilary
New Zealand**

At a recent parents evening, a teacher informed me that my 12-year-old daughter was having difficulty with her punctuation. I think she's rather good at it. Only the other day she texted her friend a picture of an ejaculating penis which she had created from brackets, apostrophes full stops and semi colons.

**T. Barnes
Chiswick**

A sign outside my bookmakers says 'Open every Sunday 11-5' Now I know for a fact that he is open on Sunday afternoons but he won't take my bet.

**Dave Stuttard
Warrington**

Last week I stopped at Watford Gap service station on the M1, and was amazed to see that their restaurant had a special offer - soup and a roll, down from £2.99 to £2.92. Has any reader seen a more unspectacular offer of anything?

**P. Mathews
Sherringham**

* Have you seen a more shit reduction or special offer than that? Write and tell us. There's soup and a roll for ten people at Watford Gap for the best letter we receive.

Is it any wonder that professional footballers' careers are so short lived? Have you seen the way they disregard Health and Safety guidelines when placing the ball down for a corner. I have witnessed the likes of David Beckham bending at the hip, rather than keeping a straight back and bending at the knees to put the ball in the quarter arc. What sort of role model for our younger generation is that?

**Gary Warburton
e-mail**

Back in the eighties when I was working for Our Price Records, ex goodie goodie Blue Peter presenter Leslie Judd came up to the counter with a CD case for a chart album. Quick as a flash, I produced the album from under the counter and said "Here's one I made earlier." The miserable cow stormed out without a word, or her CD.

**Tony
Yapton**

They say that there's no such thing as a free lunch. Bullshit. My mate is on the dole and his three kids are all on free dinners.

**Jerome Burns
e-mail**

Last winter, the government coughed up loads of our money in cold weather payments for the old folks. Meanwhile, they were busy lighting huge bonfires made of sheep and cows. Why didn't they just give each pensioner a sheep and a cow to burn as winter fuel, thus solving two problems and saving cash.

**Andy Cranwell
Perth**

The Jordan F1 team keep coming up with zany logos to get around the ban on cigarette advertising. Instead of *Benson & Hedges*, last year their cars were bedecked with the words *Buzzin' Hornets*, whilst this year they sport *Bitten Heroes*. Next year they may like to try *Black Hockle* or *Bronchitis & Heart disease*.

C. Caroli, Blackpool

Bog standard

How about this for the poshest portable shitter you've ever laid your brown eyes upon - *the Kensington Executive* in the corporate hospitality suite at this year's British Grand Prix. Scented water, carpeted floors, scarlet drapes, potted plants and piped classical music. I'm delighted to say that even amongst all this finery I still managed to block the pan.

T. Hooper, Nottingham

Sorry States

The United States and Britain have finally apologised for their part in the slave trade in the 18th and 19th centuries, and so they should. But in the spirit of going forward, shouldn't certain African tribes apologise for cooking vicars in enormous metal cauldrons and stealing their top hats?

B. J. Holmes Rhyll

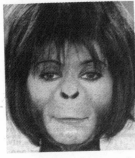

I was amazed to read how much money was spent on make up for the film *Planet of the Apes*. Surely they could have replaced Helena Bonham-Carter with that woman who plays Gail in Coronation Street and saved a fortune.

Andrew Dunn e-mail

I have been following the debate about lorry driver serial killers with interest.

I run a large international lorry firm and therefore have a reputation to keep and standards to maintain. As well as insisting my drivers wear a tie, they are required to paint the names of any women they have killed on the front of their lorries. If I find a driver with 3 or more names on the cab, they get their P45 immediately. I will not employ serial killers.

Eddie Cumbria

Webbed feat

According to National Geographic magazine, spiders' web silk is so strong that a strand the thickness of a pencil would be able to stop a Jumbo jet in flight. That is an amazing fact, but what is even more mind boggling is how strong a spider's nipsy must be to crimp the stuff off.

K. Dong Prestatyn

I see that the police recently shot a man dead for carrying a cigarette lighter in the shape of a gun. I also saw Mr. Scaramanga shot by James Bond for carrying a gun that looked like a cigarette lighter. It seems pretty clear to me that readers would do well to keep fags and firearms as separate hobbies.

Adrien Newth e-mail

I bought some cut-price videos that didn't have Kevin Spacey or Samuel L. Jackson in them. Is this a first?

Dr. Palmer e-mail

There has been a proliferation this summer of car stickers informing us that 'Dogs Die in Hot Cars'. Thanks to this advice, I saved £45 in vet bills when I had to have my alsatian put down when it got distemper.

D. Haslam e-mail

The other week I chinned a monk. I was in the park with my young son and his friend, reading Viz while they kicked a ball about. He came back crying. Apparently, he had scared some pigeons off and a monk who had been sitting there shouted at the kids. So I went over and chinned the cunt. Have any other readers punched a member of the clergy?

G. Palser Bristol

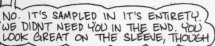

MAJOR MISUNDERSTANDING

MONTE CARLO OR BUST!

Becky Bissel and Ed Hoover had begun to find themselves arguing over the smallest things.

YOU MAKE ME SICK. ANYONE KNOWS THAT A FLEA IS TONS SMALLER THAN AN ANT!

DON'T TALK RUBBISH BECKS! THE SMALLEST THING IS DEFINITELY AN ANT!

HUNH! YOU'LL NEVER ADMIT WHEN YOU'RE WRONG WILL YOU?

THAT'S BECAUSE I NEVER AM, OF COURSE, STUPID!

THIS IS AWFUL, WE NEVER USED TO ARGUE LIKE THIS.

NO, WE NEVER ARGUED AT ALL... WHAT'S HAPPENING TO US?

WE ALWAYS USED TO AGREE...

... ABOUT EVERYTHING.

THE BIGGEST THING IS DEFINITELY AN ELEPHANT, ISN'T IT ED?

WHAT ABOUT THE BRONTOSAURUS?

HAH! OF COURSE, SILLY ME!

HA! HA! HA!

But Becky had a plan to put the spark back into their lives together. For four months she had been saving every spare penny, and now she had £4,000 - enough to take them both on a romantic dream holiday

NOW ON ITV, IT'S TIME FOR BAYWATCH. BAYWATCH IS SPONSORED BY KLEENEX.

MINT! MY FAVOURITE!

LOOK AT ALL THAT SUN, SEA AND SAND, ED. DON'T YOU WISH YOU WERE THERE?

NOT 'ARF! LOOK AT ALL THEM LOVELY ENORMOUS BOUNCING WOBBLY BIG NORKS!

HMMM...I'VE BEEN SO EXCITED ABOUT THIS HOLIDAY, I THOUGHT ED WOULD LOVE ME IF I TOOK HIM TO MONTE CARLO... BUT PERHAPS HE'D LOVE ME MORE IF I HAD HUGE PLASTIC TIT IMPLANTS FITTED.

Becky decided to talk over her dilemma over a cup of tea over at her best friend Eva's house...

IT'S YOUR BODY. GOING UNDER THE KNIFE IS NOT TO BE TAKEN LIGHTLY.

BUT ED CLEARLY LIKES BIG HOOTERS, AND I DON'T WANT TO LOSE HIM.

YES, BUT YOU WANT HIM TO LOVE YOU FOR WHAT YOU ARE, AND IF THAT MEANS GETTING SURGICALLY ENHANCED PAPS, THEN THAT'S WHAT YOU'LL HAVE TO DO.

Queen Mum in Fresh Fish-Scare

THE QUEEN Mother was last night forced to cut short a visit to the Lake District after once more choking on a fish.

Paramedics once again rushed the nation's favourite grandmother to hospital, this time in Keswick, when a bone lodged in her throat during the Penrith Cement-workers' Bazaar. During a forty minute operation, the sprightly 101-year-old sat up and chatted happily with medical staff. Doctors later announced that they had successfully removed a twenty-inch human femur, thought to belong to the late speed ace Donald Campbell, from her throat.

By our 'The Queen Mum's got another fishbone stuck in her throat' Correspondent
John Merrick

A fish - yesterday

Local fisherman Selwyn Maynard told reporters: "Fish caught in Coniston Water are filletted to remove any bits of Donald Campbell. I don't know how this one slipped through."

Fifteen years ago, the Queen Mother had to be airlifted form the Royal yacht Britannia after choking on Glen Miller's pelvis whilst eating a Dover sole.

Billy

THE BEST DOG EVER!

Jamie McMorrow

Crackers Baraccas turns Macca's Knackers into Clackers *-claim*

ITV's A-Team B.A. Baraccas, aka Big C USA VIP Mr T, last night slammed media speculation that he had gone mental and castrated ex-Beatle Paul McCartney, later turning the tragic mop-top's testicles into a popular seventies playground toy. The gold-laden buzz-topped star refused to comment when questioned at his luxury Beverly Hills cancer retreat yesterday. *-Reuters*

Crufts Laboratory Dog Show 2001: RESULTS

Best in Show
BE-BOP-A-LULA BEWILDERED WILTON WONDERLAND
Bearded Collie - Dog
Owner: Mr. and Mrs. I.C. Industries, Runcorn

Reserve Best in Show
ELEGANT BALLERINA REFINERY DUCHESS
Kerry Blue Terrier - Bitch
Owner: Capt. & Mrs. Smith-Kline Beecham, Ellesmere Port

Best Chemically-Induced Tumour in Show
PRETTY POLLY PERKINS ONCOGEN SENSATION
Spaniel (King Charles) - Dog
Owner: Mr. F. Union-Carbide, Bhopal

Best LD50 Toxicity Toy Breed
POWDERPUFF OF VOSINE GABBA-GABBA HEY
Bichon Frise - Bitch
Owner: Mrs. Marjorie Glaxo, Porton Down

Best LD50 Toxicity Utility Breed
TINKERBELL PRIDE OF CARCINOMA
Poodle (Toy) - Bitch
Owner: Mr. B. Reckitt & Mrs C. Colman, Derby

Best Smoker in Show
ROXARA PULMONARY EMPHYSEMA CHAMPAGNE CELEBRATION
Beagle (Standard) - Bitch
Owner: Mr & Mrs H. Bauer, Berkshire

Best Detergent-Blinded Working Dog
OEDIPUS LACRYMOSE CATARACTICUS OF TROY
Boxer - Dog
Owner: Mr J. Procter & Mrs S Gamble, North Shields

Best Short-Haired Terrier with its Neck Clamped in a Box
BEMUSED BOXHEAD SULTAN OF SWING
Terrier (Airedale) - Dog
Owner: Mr I. Johnson & Mr B. Johnson

Best Gundog Wired-Up to an Oscilloscope
MAGICAL SILVERHEELS VOLTAGE SURPRISE
Retriever (Golden) - Dog
Owner: Mrs. A. von Calling, Flixborough

Most Frightened Hound with Glass Cranium.
CEREBELLUM CINDERELLA-ROCKERFELLA
Saluki - Dog
Owner: Mr J. Pfizer, Hull.

in Association with the Laboratory Kennel Club

WAR! (HEURGH!)

with *Edwin Starr*

EDWIN ST★RR LETTER

George Bush said that we *'would not rest until all terrorists were brought to justice'*. I don't think my husband could have heard him. The lazy, fat cunt just lays next to me on the couch snoring, dribbling and farting.

Linda,

Congratulations to Linda, who wins a pound of sausages, a banana and a pair of knickers made from parachute silk

LAST issue, we didn't ask you to write to seventies pop legend *Edwin Starr* with your views on the current war in Afghanistan. But you did anyway, *in your thousands*. Here are a few of best letters we recieved...

Bomb rap

...**I DON'T** know what the Americans are hoping to achieve by carpet bombing Afghanistan. After all, the Afghans already have the finest rugs in the world.

D. Thackery, Hull

Yankee panky

...**TONY** Blair says Great Britain will support the USA in the current war against terrorism just as the USA supported us in WWII. Well I'll volunteer. I fancy being sent over to America to show off, laze around and fuck all the birds whilst the American troops are out getting shot at.

Glen Smith, e-mail

Spore point

...**PERHAPS** the ongoing 'mail order anthrax' scare will teach those thieving cunts who work at the Royal Mail sorting office to keep their fucking meddling hands to themselves.

Timothy Wallclock, e-mail

'Bun' Laden

...**PEOPLE** keep telling me how much my rabbit looks like Osama Bin Laden. And he keeps leaving suspicious looking pellets around the house.

Agatha Chapman, Manchester

Have YOU got a point to make about the war? Perhaps you think civilian casualties are too high a price to pay, or perhaps you've got a carrot that looks a bit like Mullah Omar. Write to the late Edwin Starr at our usual address.

BLIND *TRUNK!*

Health fears grow as Ginger whinger binger Evans drinks fucking elephant under table

BOOZY DJ Chris Evans last night hit the town on yet another 18-hour bender. But this was to be a particularly MAMMOTH session as he was accompanied by his latest drinking pal - *an African elephant!*

The millionaire DJ was forced to team up with the 8-ton party animal after his regular boozing partners, top chef Aldo Zilli and celebrity fat cunt Danny Baker, proved unable to keep pace with his drinking.

marathon

After visiting over 320 bars on their marathon pub crawl, Evans and the elephant, named Sultan by his keepers at London Zoo, took in Nelly's, London's most fashionable bun and peanut restaurant.

topic

Fellow diner Dinah Fellows said: "They were very drunk when they arrived. Evans was matching the elephant drink for drink. There was a lot of larking about and trumpeting.

mars

"Evans ordered 100 bottles of vintage port and drank them straight down. When the buns and peanuts arrived, there wasn't enough room to set them down because of all the empties, so they had to move to a larger table. I've never seen anything like it."

OUT - drinking pal chef Aldo

OUT - boozing buddy Baker
IN - elephant Sultan

They eventually ended up at West End nightclub *Stringfellows*, where they quaffed thousand-pound bottles of champagne until the early hours.

bounty

During their mind-boggling booze binge, the pair sank an incredible £4 million worth of drink, including:

THIS IS MY NEW GIRLFRIEND - A GREAT WHITE SHARK STEAK

CAREFUL. SHE'S A BIT OF A MANEATER

- 12,500 pints of lager
- 800 bottles of Laurent-Perrier pink champagne
- 100 barrels of best Bitter
- 2 vats of Chateau Lafitte 1946 red wine
- 6 tin baths of Vodka and a can of Red Bull
- 2 pints of Guinness
- 500 Formula-One size bottles of Dom Perignon.

According to witnesses, by 4am Sultan had had enough, but Evans was still going strong.

endeavour

The former *Big Breakfast* presenter made a call on his mobile, and twenty minutes later a carpenter turned up with a load of timber.

victory

Joiner Jack Churchill told us: "Evans stuck a million pounds in my top pocket, punched me in the face and told me to build a fifteen foot high table. I built the table and he drank the elephant under it. I've never seen anything like it."

"Get help

"Take my advice, Chris, or you'll soon be knocking on Evans door." That was the stark warning last night issued by the country's top alcohol expert.

Terry London, one of Britain's most experienced pub landlords said: "Doctors recommend a safe drinking limit of about 28 units per week. Chris is currently downing upwards of half a million units in a single session. Sooner or later, that sort of boozing may start to take a toll on his health."

But London, who has helped popstars, celebrities and professional footballers with their drinking during his 34-year career, says it is not too late to act. He believes this simple 3-step programme could help Evans handle his drink.

Evans - failed to turn up for work after necking 240 gallons of petrol.

Partygoers later helped sozzled tusker Sultan to a taxi. But for *Don't Forget Your Toothbrush* host Evans, the night was still young.

beagle

Amazed onlookers watched as the *TFI Friday* frontman made his way to a nearby all-night garage, where he lay on the forecourt necking £4-a-gallon Superplus unleaded petrol straight from the pump until 8 am.

Sultan turned up for the zoo two hours late the next morning, grey-faced and nursing a **jumbo-sized** hangover. Meanwhile, when Evans failed to show for his daily breakfast programme on Virgin radio, bosses blamed illness.

bosprey

However, the ginger star, looking frail and wearing twenty pairs of sunglasses, was later spotted leaving his local Waitrose store at the wheel of a dumper truck loaded with Alka Seltzer.

for Evans sake"
- says booze expert

CHRIS'S THREE STEPS TO EVANS

Step 1 Alcohol is a poison, and when it enters the blood through the stomach wall it does untold harm. If you're knocking back that much booze, give yourself a chance. Drink a pint of milk and have have some toast before you go out. And keep your stomach lined with a bag of crisps every ten pints throughout the binge.

Step 2 Keep a track of what you're drinking, and if possible use the 1-2-3 system. One of your first drink, two of your second, three of your third and so on. For example: 1 pint of lager, followed by 2 pints of bitter, followed by 3 bottles of pernod, and so on. And always finish the booze session with a pint of water.

Step 3 The morning after the night before. It's an old wives' tale that what makes you bad makes you better, but it's true nonetheless. As soon as you wake up, examine your pillow and eyebrows for congealed evidence of what you had the night before, and then hit the off licence for the hair of the dog.

"I've been there ...and it's HELL!"

One DJ's Battle to Beat the Booze -in his own words

SOMEONE who knows only too well what Evans is going through is fellow DJ *Barry Malpas,* and last night he warned the ginger millionaire: "Don't make the same mistakes I made."
In 1979, Malpas had the radio world at his feet, but a battle with the bottle nearly lost him his livelihood, family and health.

I had it all. I was a young man, just 38, the traffic reporter on BBC Radio Solent's drivetime show. It was a job most people could only dream about, and I thought it would last forever.

weekend

Drinking didn't seem to be a problem in the early days. I never gave it a second thought. Sure, I'd have a couple of pints of a weekend, like most people. But I wasn't like most people any more. I was the voice of traffic congestion in the Southampton area, mixing with celebrities on a daily basis, and it was getting harder and harder to keep my feet on the ground.

swift

It's easy to say no to a swift half at lunchtime with a friend, isn't it. But let me tell you, it's a little more difficult to turn down the offer when the person asking you out is Mike d'Abo out of Manfred Mann's Earth Band, or ex-Anglia TV anchorman Paul Lavers. Before I knew it, I was caught up on the celebrity merry-go-round. My swift half on the occasional lunchtime was now every Friday, and my two or three pints at the weekend had become three or four. Without me realising it, my drinking was spiralling out of control. Like Evans, I thought I could handle it. I played hard, but I worked hard too.

But Barry didn't realise he was burning the candle at both ends, and something had to snap. The hammerblow finally fell one Friday afternoon after a heavy drinking session with TV star Mr Bennett.

He'd been on the mid-morning show plugging a new series of Take Hart, and we went out for a swift half. Before I knew it, that swift half had become an all-lunchtime booze binge and I'd necked two halves. It was time to go on air, and my head was swimming.

swallow

I sat in the studio to do my report and the red light came on. I remember a lorry had jack-knifed on the A336 at Netley Marsh, and there were slight delays for people heading for the Cowes Ferry. Routine stuff; no problem for a professional broadcaster on top of his game. But I'd had the equivalent of a pint of lager less than five hours

before, and the inevitable happened. My relentless partying had finally caught up with me. I announced: 'Slight delays for people heading for the Fowes Kerry.' I immediately corrected myself, but the damage was done.

spit

I realised what everyone around me had known for a long time. My drinking was out of control and if I didn't do something it was going to cost me my job, my family and my health.

Six weeks later, Malpas was made redundant. The official reason given was that BBC Radio Solent had pooled its Travel news resources with BBC Radio Portsmouth, but inside, Barry knew the real reason. The BBC couldn't afford to have a beer-swilling hellraiser on the air. He'd become a liability. His booze madness had cost him his job.

walkin'

With the help of his wife Pat, Barry struggled to pull his life back together, and after a twenty-two year spell as security man at Everything's a Pound in Hedge End, he finally managed to break back into showbusiness.

I confronted my booze demons, and eventually got my drinking under control. I'm back on the radio again and life's never been sweeter. I've been given a second chance and I'm not going to throw it all away this time, I can tell you.

And Barry has this message for his troubled fellow jock Chris Evans:

"If I can do it, you can. I only hope Billie can show the patience and understanding that my Pat showed in bringing me through this nightmare."

• *Barry Malpas* presents 'Your Favourite Songs' every night from 2-6 am on Romsey Hospice's closed-loop radio system.

Say Goodbye to Inadvertent Penile Glimpsing with your...

FREE Winky

GENTLEMEN. It's Christmas, we're all going to have a bit to drink, and inevitably we're going to find ourselves using the gents. And when we're standing next to another man in the stalls, there's always a chance that we may accidentally catch a sideways glimpse of his genitals.

There's literally nothing worse, and what's more, worrying about such a momentary slip can easily ruin a perfectly good night in the pub.

Well, worry no more, because here are your fantastic free Viz *Winky Blinkers*™ - patented devices which safely and discreetly prevent unintentional organ sightings in the urinals.

Pop them on whenever you go to the toilets. Then you can relax and enjoy your wee, secure in the knowledge that should you inadvertently look left or right, you'll see nothing more upsetting than a set of golf clubs or a steam locomotive. Should the man beside you do likewise, he'll receive a stern warning to face the front.

Your free Winky Blinkers™ are suitable for use in pubs, clubs, and any public convenience. What's more, they're small enough to slip into your pocket, so make sure you don't go out without them.

Instructions

Cut around the solid lines, fold along the dotted ones, and assemble the blinkers and head strap assembly with glue as shown in the diagram.

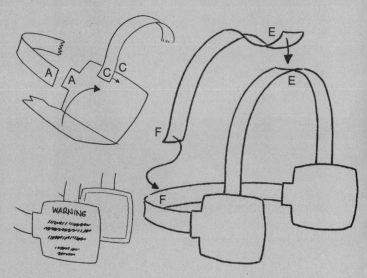

C

WARNING!

IF YOU ARE READING THIS, YOU ARE LOOKING IN THE WRONG DIRECTION.

PLEASE FACE FORWARD AND CONTINUE YOUR WEE

A

B

A

D

Blinkers ™

BEFORE

Ensures Cock-Free Field of Vision This Xmas! Will Not Impede Hockling, Farting or Jocular Heterosexual Smalltalk!

AFTER

"In my song, I say you've gotta have *faith*, but in fact, what you've gotta have is *Winky Blinkers.*"

George M, California

"If I'd have had a pair of Winky Blinkers 30 years ago, I'd never have seen that farmer's cock which he pushed through a hole in the lavatory wall, let alone prodded it, and I could have been the Pope instead of a poxy Bishop."

Rt Rev. Bishop of D, Durham

A

C

E

Viz **Winky Blinkers**

F

Viz **Winky Blinkers**

E

F

B

D

NAZI CARAVAN

incorporating EXTREME RIGHT-WING MOTORHOME

£3.60

Issue 112   August 2001

INCREASE YOUR LEBENSRAUM
move up to a 6 berth this summer

HEIL HITCHER
the final solution in tow bars

MEIN KAMPFSITE
Professor David Irving takes us to his favourite spot

AWNINGS
the simplest way to annex your neighbour's pitch

ARYAN SPACIOUS
we review the *Panzer Pirouette* the first caravan to be awarded 5 *yellow stars*

REICH OF WAY
motoring tips for travel abroad

ON SALE NOW!

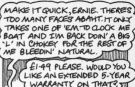

Letterbocks

letters@viz.co.uk

Star Letter

If you've got an opinion on something, or even if you haven't, write and tell what it is, or isn't, and we'll make it worth your while. This month we've got a copy of the hilarious cartoon 'The Family Guy' for every letter published. So that's our Christmas shopping done. Write to - Letterbocks, Viz Comic, PO. Box 1PT, Newcastle upon Tyne, NE99 1PT

Who says doing Christmas shopping early avoids the crush? Last year, I did mine a full 12 months in advance, and the shops were just as busy as ever.

Gavin McKernan
Ballycastle

I had a dream last night that I had used the last piece of toilet roll. Today, after having a morning 'log out', that very same scenario occured for real. It's reassuring to know, that in this time of misery and uncertainty, dreams do sometimes come true.

Becky Morris
Australia

Letterbocks
Viz Comic
P.O. Box 1PT
Newcastle-upon-Tyne
NE99 1PT

Me and my mates have just started a sweepstake and wonder if your readers would like to join in. We put a pound in and guess how many times irritating pretend chef Ainsley Harriett gropes the female contestants in each episode of Ready, Steady, Cook! Sorry, 37, 41 and 43 have already gone.

Doug Richards
Wolverhampton

I read somewhere that if certain keywords, like bomb, terrorism, etc, are used in e-mails, the British Intelligence service get to 'listen in' on that e-mail. If this is the case, given that I've already mentioned such words, do you think you could find the bastard that nicked my car?

Dave Webster
e-mail

The Bank of Scotland proudly boasts the motto 'A Friend for Life.' Imagine my surprise upon running into £2000 debt when two burly youths beat me up and repossessed all my furniture. Some fucking friend that is.

David Maxwell
e-mail

I recently had to stop at Barton Park Lorry Services on the A1 for petrol. I have never seen such a tailor-made place for the truckers to hide the murdered bodies of female hitch hikers. I wouldn't be surprised if there were acid baths available to aid body dispersal. Have any other readers seen a more likely spot for trucker atrocities?

Oliver scull
e-mail

PS. It also had the best selection of grumble mags I've seen this side of Amsterdam, but then again it would, wouldn't it?

I think readers will be interested to see from this headline in the San Francisco Chronicle that the Americans take a dim view of bestiality, even when the normally all-exonerating excuse of road rage is pleaded.

Road-rage dog tosser sentenced to 3 years

Judge throws book

Andy Burr
California

How do lesbian couples put up with each other when every two weeks in four, one of them's a rag-hag? And what about the one in four couples whose menstrual cycles are synchronised? They must go through the crockery like a Greek wedding with angel dust kebabs.

Murf
e-mail

If lorry drivers all have CB radios, then why don't they use them instead of driving side by side on duel carriageways, gassing to each other about their latest murders?

Dave Chamberlain
Leicester

Is it just me, or has Angela Griffin got a dog's cock for a tongue?

Alex Beech
Coalville

Considering her recent behaviour, is there anyone left who believes Britney Spears is still a virgin? She could confirm it once and for all by posing for a few close up pink shots of that supposedly unbreached hymen. So come on, Britney, let's settle this nonsense once and for all.

T. Woods
e-mail

Having sent three letters to your magazine and never having one published, it is with great sadness that I must announce my resignation from writing to Letterbox.

Jules Faber
e-mail

Bob Geldof is a cunt. I once sat behind the unkempt, anti-establishment knight at Heathrow Airport on his way to Switzerland. Proclaiming that 'only the fucking English queue' he proceeded to sit on his arse sending two middle-aged, pony-tailed, pot-bellied rocker hangers on to queue for him, then pushing in like a kraut as they got to the front.

Anonymous
e-mail

How do we know that Steven Hawking is clever? Someone could have just programmed him.

Mike Woods
London

If Elton John is so fucking rich, how come his wig looks like it's been twocked of a piss-sodden tramp?

James Lennox
Glasgow

PS My dad is a vicar, so please just print my initial if you publish my letter as he would be shocked to discover I had written it.

*Certainly, Tim.

WIG WATCH

Sender:
Ian Glover, e-mail

It must be five years or so since you printed that black and white picture of the bloke kissing that bird's arse. Surely technology has advanced since then to allow you to print it in digitally remastered colour.

Geeze
e-mail

★ Well, Geeze, are you in for a treat. Here it is, not only in remastered colour, but also in 3D. Watch out for the moving hologram of it in issue 130.

They say you are what you eat. I couldn't agree more. I have been a cannibal and a person all my life.

Chief Umbongo Okwekwe
Papua New Guinea

Imagine if Fatima Whitbread's tits had beer coming out of them. Just imagine!

R. Howden
Leeds

People should not say horrible things about the terrorist Osama Bin Laden. They are simply bringing themselves down to his level.

H. Francis
Cardiff

I found this picture in an American phonebook a while ago. Take a look at it for a few seconds then turn it upside down and cover the glass and the lady's head. Has anyone else found any hidden porn in phonebooks?

Kev Pryor
Leicester

J. FLOORING
01273 697584

WIG WATCH
Sender: Dean Webb, Paignton

SUICIDAL SYD — HE'S ALWAYS TRYING TO POP HIS CORK!

I'M SO HAPPY, READERS. I'VE FOUND A BRAND NEW GRUMBLE MAG STUFFED UNDER A HEDGE ON MY WAY HOME FROM SCHOOL...

...I CAN'T WAIT TO SEE ALL THE NUDIE LADIES.

MUCH LATER...

BAH! IT WAS ONLY AN IKEA CATALOGUE.

IT TOOK ME TWO HOURS TO KNOCK ONE OUT OVER A PICTURE OF A PINE CD RACK. YOU'VE NO IDEA HOW BAD I FEEL...

GLOOM!

...I THINK I'LL KILL MYSELF.

THIS LOT ARE QUEUING FOR THIS YEAR'S 'MUST HAVE' TOY.

I'LL PUSH TO THE FRONT AND BUY THE LOT. THEY'LL RIP ME TO SHREDS! HEH! HEH!

TOYS AM US

PUSH

I'LL TAKE ALL THE HARRY POTTER TOYS YOU'VE GOT, PLEASE.

CERTAINLY SIR. THAT'LL BE £100,000 PLEASE.

HEH-HEH! ANY MINUTE NOW...

WHAT'S GOING ON? WHY HAVEN'T I BEEN SET UPON AND TORN LIMB FROM LIMB?

WE'RE NOT AFTER THE HARRY POTTER STUFF...

...WE'VE BEEN IN THIS QUEUE SINCE 1994. WE'RE STILL AFTER TRACY ISLAND.

BAH! I'M NOT DEAD AND I'VE SPENT A HUNDRED GRAND ON 'FLAVOUR OF THE MONTH' PLASTIC TOYS.

etc. AND SO ON.

THINGS CAN'T GET ANY WORSE!

EXCUSE ME...

I'M AN ECCENTRIC MILLIONAIRE, AND THIS IS MY HORRIBLY SPOILT SON WHO LIKES HARRY POTTER...

...IF YOU GIVE ME THOSE HARRY POTTER TOYS, I'LL GIVE YOU SOMETHING MONEY CAN'T BUY... THIS TICKET TO A SHOWBIZ CELEBRITY PARTY!

IT'S A DEAL!

HEY, I'M SO EXCITED ABOUT THIS SHOWBIZ BASH, THAT I'M ALL CHEERED UP AND NO LONGER WISH TO KILL MYSELF.

SHOWBIZ CELEBRITY PARTY HERE TODAY

OR-WIGHT! OR-WIGHT! COME IN...

...HAVE YOU BROUGHT YOUR SWIMMING TRUNKS?

It's 'BRIE' N.A.

JUBILANT scientists were last night celebrating after finally identifying the gene which determines whether or not a person likes cheese. Eggheads at the human genome project have spent years sifting through miles of DNAs, looking for the genes which make us partial to parmesan, crazy about camembert or hanker after half a pound of haloumi (a sort of Greek goat's cheese).

The gene, known as P352, is just an eighth of an inch long and is found in every cell of our bodies, according to Susan Intray, professor of genetics at Imperial College Rothbury.

population

"Although this gene is present in everybody's DNA, it is switched off in 20% of the population," said Professor Intray. "So while the majority of people are genetically programmed to like cheese, approximately one person in five can take it or leave it."

wallpaper

Scientists hope that in the next five to ten years they will be able to offer expectant mothers a test to determine whether or not their unborn children

Boffins identify cheese gene

will have a liking for cheese. Professor Intray said: "It's a very exciting time. The cheese gene opens up the possibility of identifying other DNA markers, such as those determining a liking for Scotch eggs or vol au vents."

bare

But her enthusiasm was not matched in Britain's cheesemonger community. "The scientists' argument, like some of our cheeses (such as Gouda and Emmental), is full of holes," stormed spokesman Peter Cable. "Parents who don't particularly care

for cheese will be able to choose not to go through with a pregnancy if they find they are carrying a child that would really like cheese. It's like 1984 all over again. This announcement is the thin end of a very large cheese-shaped wedge. Of cheese."

tigre

Many cheesemongers believe they could face financial ruin if Professor Intray's pre-natal test becomes a reality: "All small shopkeepers are feeling

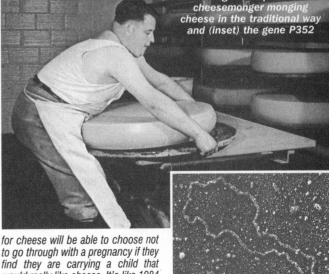

A thing of the past? - a cheesemonger monging cheese in the traditional way and (inset) the gene P352

the pinch," said Luton cheesemonger Frank Wainscotting. "I've been monging cheese for forty years. My father and grandfather monged cheese before me. Monging is all I know. If nobody wants cheese any more, I may have to start monging fish. Or iron."

FRU T. BUNN the MASTER BAKER & HIS GINGERBREAD SEX DOLLS

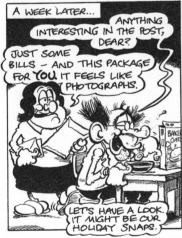

Smooch at Ten

ITN gets physical in battle of the newshounds

THE RATINGS WAR between the BBC's *Ten O'clock News* and ITV's *News at Ten* is set to hot up - when ITV screens the first *gay kiss* between newsreaders later this week.

In the shocking scene, viewers will see veteran anchorman Sir Trevor McDonald finish a report on a Guatemalan earthquake, before turning to give a lingering kiss on the lips to

EXCLUSIVE

Bevitt - denying gay kiss is gimmick, yesterday

Murnaghan- kiss

Witchell - bad boy

Ford - astronaut

Derham - baby

co-presenter Dermot Murnaghan.

ITN bosses are bracing themselves for an onslaught of complaints when 10 million viewers watch the controversial clinch at the close of the episode to be broadcast on Wednesday.

bolster

But they last night denied that it was merely a cheap ploy to bolster viewing figures for the flagship show.

"This gay kiss is no gimmick," insisted ITN chief Ian Bevitt. "We like to think that our news programmes reflect real life issues, and like it or not homosexual relationships are a part of everyday life."

duvet

Meanwhile, a TV insider hinted that ITN has many more dramatic plots in the pipeline to keep viewers on the edge of their seats.

pillow

He revealed top secret plans including a mystery virus sweeping through the newsroom

Dermott and Trevor - on-screen smacker could prove winner in the ratings war. Yesterday

and Katie Derham having an illegitimate baby to a mystery weatherman in the Autumn.

"It's a cracking plot," he told us. The father's identity will be revealed in a special double-length edition on Christmas Day.

dog

Meanwhile BBC bosses denied using spoiling tactics and dismissed as "pure coincidence" reports that they are planning to steal ITN's thunder. News chief Tony Hall is believed to have given the green light to a sensational two-part cliff-hanger starting on Tuesday night.

Viewers will see heart-throb newsman George

Alagaiah trapped in a blazing studio after BBC bad boy 'Nasty Nicholas' Witchell discards a cigarette in a pile of news reports.

fist

The public will only find out if he escapes the inferno by watching Wednesday's Ten O'clock News - scheduled directly against McDonald and Murnaghan's gay kiss.

feltch

The BBC has recently been under pressure to make its news presentation more realistic. Over the past few years, it has lost viewers with such far-fetched storylines as a lesbian siege, Anna Ford marrying an astronaut and Jill Dando being murdered by a roller-skating Freddie Mercury impersonator.

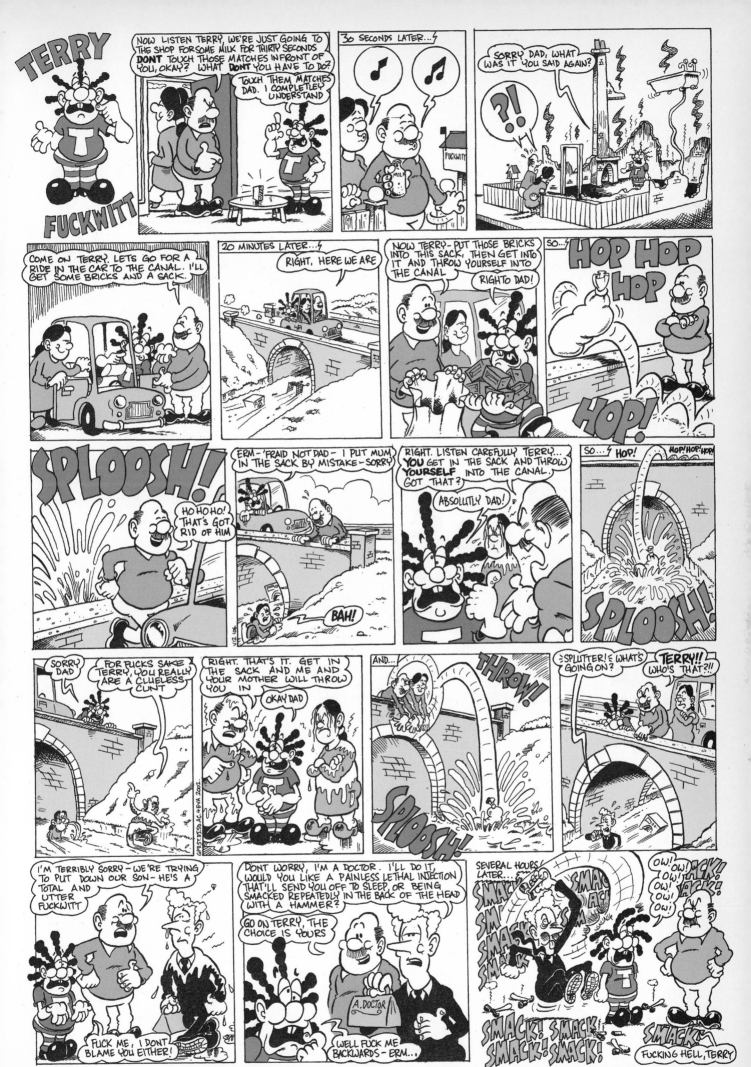

111

GOSH, THESE ARE LOVELY CREATURES

WHAT A DEPRESSING THOUGHT, I CANT AFFORD A TICKET TO AUSTRALIA, AND I'LL NEVER GET TO SEE THEM IN THEIR NATURAL ENVIROMENT...

...I THINK I'LL KILL MYSELF

AT THE STATION... RIGHT READERS, I'M GOING TO GET A MORNING TRAIN PACKED WITH ANGRY, STRESSED COMMUTERS AND GO THROUGH THE ENTIRE REPERTOIRE OF RINGING TONES ON MY MOBILE AT FULL VOLUME

SOMEBODY WILL SNAP AND BEAT ME TO DEATH JUST LIKE MICHEAL DOUGLAS IN "FALLING DOWN"

SMACK!

SORRY, ALL OUR VIRGIN TRAINS HAVE BEEN CANCELLED DUE TO GROSS INCOMPETENCE

BUT AS COMPENSATION HERE'S A FREE AIRLINE TICKET TO AUSTRALIA

HEY, GREAT!

NEXT DAY... LADIES AND GENTLEMEN, WE WILL SHORTLY BE LANDING IN AUSTRALIA

TOP! I'M GOING TO GET TO SEE SOME KANGAROOS ANY TIME NOW!

LAND!

JUST ONE CASE OF ECONOMY CLASS DEEP VEIN THROMBOSIS TODAY, BRUCE

BONZER COBBER!

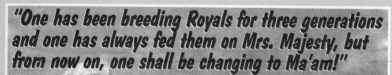

"One has been breeding Royals for three generations and one has always fed them on Mrs. Majesty, but from now on, one shall be changing to Ma'am!"

Mrs. Q.E.t. Q.M.
Clarence House

HEAD CHEF

By our Bizarre X-rays correspondent **Hans Roentgen**

Man had mixer in skull and DIDN'T KNOW!

DOCTORS thought there had been a mix-up when they looked at X-rays of a man's skull and saw a ten-inch long Kenwood Chef *lodged inside his cranium!*

casualty

Incredibly, 34-year-old Dennis Woodglue had walked around for four weeks with the appliance in his head without feeling a thing. It was only when the unemployed carpet salesman went to his local casualty department complaining of a whirring noise that amazed doctors discovered the cause.

ER

In a touch-and-go operation lasting 12 hours, surgeons at the *Queen's Medical Centre* in Nottingham managed to switch the mixer off before removing it from Mr. Woodglue's head.

Holby City

The freak accident happened whilst Dennis was making himself a cup of tea at his home in Clifton.

"I opened the wrong cupboard to get my mug, and a load of pots and stuff fell on my head," he recalled. "I put it all back and thought nothing of it, but the mixer must have penetrated my skull and gone right inside. There was no pain or anything."

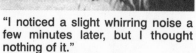

"I noticed a slight whirring noise a few minutes later, but I thought nothing of it."

Denton Town

It was nearly a month until the amazing discovery was made.

"He's very lucky to be alive," said neurosurgeon Dr Hans Watchstrap. "Miraculously, the whisks only caused damage to an area of the brain primarily concerned with pub quiz trivia. One millimetre to the left and he could have been blinded or paralysed. As it is, he is simply left unable to remember the names of the seven dwarves."

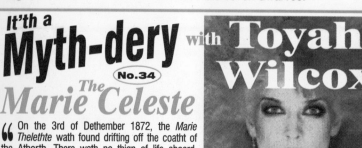

It'th a Myth-dery with Toyah Wilcox

No.34
The Marie Celeste

" On the 3rd of Dethember 1872, the *Marie Thelethte* wath found drifting off the coatht of the Athorth. There wath no thign of life aboard. Everything appeared to be normal, clothethth lay folded in the crew'th quarterth and breakfatht lay therved but uneaten in the galley. In the Captain'th cabin, the log wath filled in and nothing out of the ordinary wath reported. There wath no thign of any thtruggle.

What happened on board the Marie Thelethte? Why did the crew to thimply dithappear? And why ith it none were ever found...? "

...it'th a Myth-dery, oh, it'th a Myth-dery, we're thtill thearching, for the truth...

Netht week - *The Loch Neth Monthter*

THE THEFT FAMILY ROBINSON

KNOCK KNOCK

READ YOUR PALM, DEARIE?

YOU WILL BE VISITED BY A TALL, DARK STRANGER

HE WILL RELIEVE YOU OF A GREAT WEIGHT THAT'S BEEN SITTING OVER YOUR HEAD FOR MANY YEARS

OOH, WILL HE? THAT'S NICE

EEH. THE THIEVING BASTARD'S HAD THE SLATES OFF ME ROOF

ALFONSO ROBINSON ROOFER

Twisted FEAR-STARTER!

TRADITIONAL old-fashioned phobias like the fear of snakes, flying and confined spaces are giving way to more twenty-first century fears such as mobile phones, the internet and microscooters, according to the results of a survey published yesterday.

But by far and away the most common fear amongst the British public is **Flintophobia** - an irrational terror of Keith Flint out of The Prodigy.

public

Researchers from the University of South Hedgely were amazed to discover that **one in seven** members of the public were terrified of the spikey-haired head-rubbing pop singer.

practice

"More people were scared of Keith Flint than were scared of heights, knives and moths put together," said Professor Ridley Fairnington.

"One woman even had to send her husband upstairs to check for him in case he was in the bath."

sherman

Other subjects couldn't even bear to look at pictures of him; one

woman was shown the video for Firestarter and shat herself.

j. arthur

"Phobias evolved in caveman times, as valuable survival instincts," everything's-a-pound psychiatrist Dr. Raj Persaud told us.

ham

"Being scared of dinosaurs meant that a stone age person would live longer and stand a better chance of passing on their genes. In the same way, someone who would run away from Keith Flint is more likely to avoid having him stick his tongue out at them."

barclays

"Those flintophobia genes are then passed on to future generations, and so the cycle continues," he waffled.

river

Pennystretcher psychologist Oliver James

Flint Strikes Terror into British Psyche

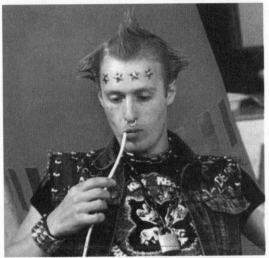

Frightening Flint - Top of the Fear Pops

offered advice for people with flintophobia: "Start by looking for a few seconds at a drawing of Keith. Once you can manage that, look at a photograph and listen to a bit of one of his records, such as Smack my Bitch Up. After a few weeks of this desensitization you should be able to sit through the Firestarter video, or even handle Keith Flint, with no problems."

NO SEX, PLEASE! -we're vicars

BRITAIN is at last shaking off its image as a hotbed for sex vicars. That's the finding of a new report commissioned by the General Synod.

Researchers from Hull University questioned over ten thousand Church of England priests, asking if they had been convicted of a sex crime in the last twelve months and found that only 82% had. This compares to 94% in 1999.

Author of the report, Professor Kid Chocolate said: "These figures mark a welcome trend. A few

years ago, you couldn't open your Sunday paper without reading a dozen stories about sex vicars. These days you'd be lucky if you found ten."

convicted

The Bishop of Fulchester, the Right Reverend Derek Nonseworth also welcomed the findings.

"It shows that the Church of England is finally putting its house in order," he said.

"Everyone is doing their best. I myself have not been convicted of a single sex crime this year, merely cautioned 8 times for masturbating in public and stealing ladies' underwear from clotheslines."

*What sort of sex case is **your** vicar? Send us a photo and a brief resume of his last 3 convictions. The sex-est vicar will get £50 for his steeple fund.*

POP IS HELPING PREPARE FOR TOMORROWS DINNER...

RIGHT GERALD. I'VE HEARD QUITE ENOUGH SEXUAL REFERENCES ABOUT YOUR GRAVY. WILL YOU DO THE TURKEY NOW?

YES, DEAR, OF COURSE

OH YES. THIS IS A FINE BIRD...

SOME FINE ASSED BIRD WITH BIIIIG JUICY TITTIES! MMMN - HMMMN!!

OH GOD.

OOH YEAH! I'M GONNA PART 40' FINE ASSED LITTLE BIRD LEGS AND STUFF YO' LITTLE CHICKEN PUSS-EH TILL IT ACHES BAY-BEH - YEAH!

FOR GODS SAKE GERALD. I'LL DO THE TURKEY. YOU PUT THE POTATOES IN THE OVEN

RIGHT, LETS SEE... GAS MARK SIX... I'LL TURN UP THE HEAT...

YEAH-I'LL TURN UP THE HEAT BAY-BEH, TILL YOU'RE SOOO HOT- THEN I'LL SLIDE IT INSIDE RIGHT UP TO THE SPUDS!

GERALD!! GO AND DO THE DECORATIONS - NOW!!

I'LL PUT THE PAPER CHAINS UP DEAR... I'LL PUT THEM RIGHT UP! OOOH BABEH! RIGHT UP AS FAR AS THEY WILL GO - AND WHEN YOU SCREAM FOR ME TO STOP, I'LL PUT THEM UP FURTHER BAYBEH!

THAT'S IT! YOU'VE RUINED MY CHRISTMAS! I'M GOING TO BED RIGHT NOW AND YOU'RE SLEEPING ON THE SOFA

SCUFF-SCUFF!

EH? WHATS THAT?

GASP! IT'S FATHER CHRISTMAS!

HO HO HO! YOU'VE GOT A BIT OF A TIGHT CHIMNEY THERE...

...SUCH A SWEET, TIGHT LITTLE CHIMNEY

SLOOP SLOOP GULP!

UGH UGH UGH UGH

TCHH! SOME OF US ARE TRYING TO SLEEP.

 **TINRIBS**

11-YEAR OLD TOMMY TAYLOR'S BEST FRIEND WAS A REMARKABLE ROBOT CALLED TINRIBS

IT'S THE SCHOOL CAROL CONCERT TODAY, TINRIBS

A SQUIRT OF OIL IN YOUR VOICE BOX WILL HAVE YOU SINGING LIKE A LARK.

HI. I'M BARBIE

AT SCHOOL

OH LITTLE TOWN OF BETHLEHEM..

HI. I'M BARBIE. I LOVE YOU VERY MUCH.

SNIFFLE THAT ROBOT'S BEAUTIFUL ELECTRONIC SINGING HAS MOVED ME SO MUCH, I SHALL CANCEL ALL LESSONS FOR A YEAR

INSTEAD, WE WILL CELEBRATE CHRISTMAS EVERY DAY

BAH! CHRISTMAS INDEED. WHAT A LOAD OF COCK.

WATCH ME SPOIL THEIR PATHETIC CAROL CONCERT PARTY

HEH HEH! I'VE SMASHED THE CHRISTMAS TREE FAIRY INTO SMITHEREENS

STAMP STOMP

THAT'LL DAMPEN THEIR YULETIDE JOY

OH NO, LOOK! THE CHRISTMAS TREE FAIRY IS BROKEN! WE CAN'T HAVE CHRISTMAS WITHOUT THE FAIRY

WE'LL HAVE TO CANCEL ALL FESTIVITIES AND DO SUMS INSTEAD

WAIT, HEADMASTER - MY ROBOT PAL WILL MAKE AN IDEAL REPLACEMENT FAIRY FOR THE CHRISTMAS TREE...

...IF MR SNODWORTHY WOULD KINDLY HELP WITH THE COSTUME

AND - WE'VE MADE SOME LOVELY FAIRY WINGS OUT OF STRIPS OF SKIN PEELED OFF MR SNODWORTHY'S TORSO...

AGONY

...AND A BONE RIPPED OUT OF MR SNODWORTHY'S ARM PROVIDES A SMASHING WAND.

HI. I'M BARBIE. I LOVE YOU VERY MUCH

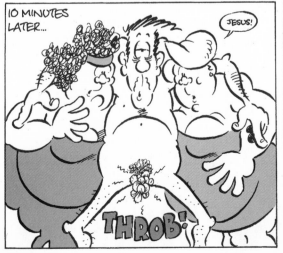

POLIO STREET MIXED INFANT SCHOOL REUNION

EEH, DOLLY. IT ONLY SEEMS LIKE YESTERDAY WE WAS HERE.

IT WAS ONLY YESTERDAY, ADA.

WE COME ON THE WRONG DAY, REMEMBER?

MIND, DOLLY. THERE GETS FEWER OF US EVERY YEAR AT THESE DO'S, DON'T THERE.

DO'S, YES. THERE DOES.

THERE'LL ONLY BE US TWO LEFT SOON.

THERE IS ONLY US TWO, ADA. THERE'S ONLY BEEN YOU AND ME LEFT SINCE 1971.

1971, YES. THAT WAS A BAD YEAR. IT TOOK A LOT OF THE OLD 'UNS, 1971 DID. IT WAS THE TINNED SALMON, Y'KNOW.

SALMON, YES.

I NEARLY SUCCUMBED TO THE 1971 SALMON MYSELF.

I DIDN'T DO ANOTHER SOLID DUTY TILL SILVER JUBILEE YEAR.

YES.

EEH.

MIND YOU, I'M NOT SAD ALL THEM OTHERS ARE GONE. GOOD RIDDANCE TO BAD RUBBISH, THAT'S WHAT I SAY.

I NEVER LIKED ANY OF 'EM.

ME NEITHER.

THAT DOLLY EARNSHAW WAS THE WORST.

GOT VD OFF A BIG BLACK MAN, SHE DID.

YES, DREADFUL.

FANCY.

THE SLATTERN.

OOH, SHE WAS A BAD LOT, SHE WAS.

I WONDER WHAT HAPPENED TO HER.

WAS. YES.

EEH. I DON'T KNOW.

WAIT A MINUTE, ADA. I DO! IT'S ME! I'M DOLLY EARNSHAW!

OOH, YES. THAT'S RIGHT. WHAT DID HAPPEN TO YOU?

EEH, I DON'T KNOW. PERHAPS I MOVED AWAY OR DIED OR SUMMAT.

SHORTLY...

EEH. THERE'S A BOBBY STOOD STANDING BY ME GATE.

SORRY LOVE. WE'VE EVACUATED THE STREET DUE TO A FRACTURED GAS MAIN. EVERYONE'S GONE DOWN THE CHURCH HALL TILL IT GETS MENDED.

EEH. LET ME PAST. I'VE STILL GOT ME OLD ANDERSON SHELTER IN THE GARDEN. JERRY DIDN'T SCARE ME AWAY IN THE WAR AND HE'S NOT GOING TO SCARE ME AWAY NOW.

SO...

EEH. THIS OLD SHELTER BRINGS BACK SOME HAPPY MEMORIES. SITTING THERE WITH ME MAM, EATING ITMA SANDWICHES AND LISTENING TO POWDERED EGG ON THE WIRELESS.

EEH! I'VE NOT BEEN DOWN HERE SINCE 1940, AND IT'S JUST LIKE I REMEMBER.

HANG ON - THERE'S SOMETHING MOVING.

... EEH, ADA. IS THAT YOU?

MAM!? WHAT ARE YOU DOING DOWN HERE?

JUST WAITING. I'VE BEEN SAT HERE MORE THAN 60 YEARS.

EEH. HAPPEN YOU DIDN'T HEAR THE ALL CLEAR SIREN AT THE END OF THE BLITZ.

AYE.

ANYWAY, YOU'LL NEVER GUESS WHO I'VE JUST SEEN, MAM... DOLLY EARNSHAW!

SHE NEVER!

EEH! SHE GOT VD, YOU KNOW.

SHE DID. OFF A BIG BLACK MAN, AND THAT'S TRUE.

E-mail
profanisaurus@
letterbocks
.com

Chipperfield n. ...ing you get off a bou... for no good reason.

clitty litter n. Vagina... detritus in the dri... a lady's du...

clot...

return fire n. Splashback.

reveille n. An early morning brass eye fanfare delivered with military precision that makes your company jump out of bed.

ripping up rags sim. Descriptive of the sound of a long drawn out fart...

chimp dominatrix of the same name.

mechanical dandruff n. Royal Air Force 'crabs.

fanny badger n. See Blackbeard's ghost.

fasturbation n. Emergency, hurried self-abuse.

femtex n. Hormone-based explosive which becomes ...g coil pots. The arse.

mountbattens n. Small fragments of shattere... turds fou... ...ank... toilet... penil...

...holster n. A roman-...erm for a lady's ...ath. "Felicity was pow-...ss to resist. His eyes ...ed into hers like sap-...ires. His strong arms ...folded her tender body ...s she felt herself being ...swept away in a whirlwind of passion. Then, she knelt before him and ...before you could say ...ife', he had stuck his ...inch Charlie...

jizzard n. blizzard... ...etters page of ...suffe... or a small ad being American...

jizzbolt n. ...group... ambassador's... and dis... immaculately trimmed bush. its of...

arse like the top of a sauce bottle sim. A less than clean ...ectum. One where slight ...illages and leaks have ...ed in situ, and which will ...ve to be picked clean.

four-man bob n. ...speedily eject... Possibly rocking ...ards and forwards 20m ...ers before coming...

...moreders

...witching ho...nding over ...binrake. pick up some lawn... dog'st can cause 30 de... be raised simulata-neously.

docking v. The rolling of one's fiveskin over another chap's hat. A clash of heads.

dripping like a fucked fridge sim. Of a lady, to be sexual-ly aroused. "I'm in the mood for love/ Simply beco... you're near me/ and... er you're nea'...

flapmonger n. ...mongs flaps. A ta... pimp.

...footwell flavour n. dinner to...stroying ar... blimplants... g that appe... surgically enha... ...heater. fruit

bush meat n. Meat found under bushes.

...nic mutton n. A matur... ...aying to lo...

wanker's block n. ...plete absence of imag... or inspiratio... so impressive that a... are rendered speech... in their presence.

Inman's twitch n. brisk, staccato, buttock clenched walk to the toilet when one is attempting to prevent turtle egress. From it adopted by 70s sit-...or John Inman. A sacrificial T.

porn glare n. The cru... frustrating shaft of l... which partially obsc... spreadeagled bir... double page sp... art pamphlet strives for vinegar...

rollover week n. A... when the painters are in.

scum shovel n. Any form of...

fish fryer's Descriptive... piss... that forms... trough at sh... ...cessitates having motorcycle outrider.

after dinner bint n. A... you have to take o... ...fuck.

witch doctor's rattle n. descriptive of a woman with a nice personality. A monk's pin-up.

woodpecker n. A woman who performs rapid, hands-fre... ...tio. From the move... ...bird's head a... ...son and nana Rob... 'Stewpot' Ste... ...dio 1 Junior Choice, 1...

tickle your pip v. T... aroused sexually by P... Philips or Terry-Thom...

change n. During intercourse, decide to play the B-si...arm From the only station From the London Undergrou... where it is possible t... change from the Pink line (Hammersmith & City) to the Brown line (Bakerloo).

cheapies n. Schoolboy sexual thrills. "Miss Pollard bent down to pick up the chalk, ...iving William his che...

valentines day porridge n. Semen-o-lina, spaff, spangle, snedge, gunk.

Prof. Fuck. ...got lots of bits of shit ...se. I know that they are ca... ...uld I refer to the hai...

blooper 1 n. An actor's mistake which provides Dennis Norden something to do while waits to die. 2 n...

tossed salad n. US. Anal sex between male pris on-ers. "'More tossed salad, Mr Archer?' 'No thanks, M... Big, I'm completely stuffed.'"

tramps delight n. Low cost cider.

truncheon voucher n. A ticket to the policeman's ball. A constabulary bribe.

...un to the eggs adj. Engaged ...r mugg...ative sex. Up...tices. ...discover has... ...r the head an... out of your w...esman. ...rning after yo...

Armani & Navy n. Poorly-made imitation designer clothes purchased from a ...market.

Hello. This issue's guests are Jeremy Irons, Sandi Toksvig and Hannah Gordon. And our first word is...

banjo cleaner... BANJO clea... ...Jer...ush through n. the con-sequence of buying very cheap 'Economy Brand'

A banjo cleaner ... the term given to very brisk lady's w... is derived from the f... during the height of the lady appears to...

Thank you, Jere... Sandi

double fare n. Or fat arse takes up... on a dodg...

Blackbeard's ghost n. A tri-angular, white, spooky apparition occasionally glimpsed by the one-eyed ...about in one's crow's nest.

Robin Cook... sparsely vegetated minge. A grate...